M000282405

CHRISTMAS IN MARIPOSA

To Roger:

CHRISTMAS IN MARIPOSA

Sketches of Canada's Legendary Little Town

Jamie Lamb

Merry Christmas 2019

from another Leacock fan.

H
HERITAGE

Victoria | Vancouver | Calgary

Copyright © 2019 Jamie Lamb

All rights reserved. No part of this publication may be reproduced, stored in a retrieval system, or transmitted in any form or by any means—electronic, mechanical, audio recording, or otherwise—without the written permission of the publisher or a licence from Access Copyright, Toronto, Canada.

Heritage House Publishing Company Ltd.
heritagehouse.ca

Cataloguing information available from Library and Archives Canada

978-1-77203-287-1 (pbk)
978-1-77203-286-4 (epub)

Edited by Lenore Hietkamp
Proofread by Marial Shea
Cover design by Jacqui Thomas
Interior design by Setareh Ashrafologhalai
Cover images: house and snow globe, by Jacqui Thomas; snowy background, by GhostlyPixels/CreativeMarket.com; holly, by Darumo Sharp/CreativeMarket.com; textured background, by noipornpan/iStockphoto.com
Poetry extract on p. 203 is from "Requiescat" by Oscar Wilde (https://www.bartleby.com/103/19.html)

The interior of this book was produced on 100% post-consumer recycled paper, processed chlorine free, and printed with vegetable based inks.

Heritage House gratefully acknowledges that the land on which we live and work is within the traditional territories of the Lkwungen (Esquimalt and Songhees), Malahat, Pacheedaht, Scia'new, T'Sou-ke, and W̱SÁNEĆ (Pauquachin, Tsartlip, Tsawout, Tseycum) Peoples.

We acknowledge the financial support of the Government of Canada through the Canada Book Fund (CBF) and the Canada Council for the Arts, and the Province of British Columbia through the British Columbia Arts Council and the Book Publishing Tax Credit.

23 22 21 20 19   1 2 3 4 5

Printed in Canada

To Jim, Ruby, and Rod Lamb—who understand
and know where the treasure is buried.

Contents

Preface

SWING THE RENTAL car to a stop by the curb at the walking trail, turn off the engine, and consider what I've done.

What I've done is fly 3,300 kilometres from Vancouver to Toronto, driven north to a tourist town on a small Ontario lake, and parked near the end of the street where I grew up. It's a long way to come just to take a walk along a shoreline street to see what memories it might spark—Christmas memories at that—but it needs to be done.

There had been a time when I knew every inch of this street. I had walked it, tricycled it, bicycled it, skateboarded it, snowshoed it, hay-ridden it, driven it in every conceivable kind of motorized conveyance. Its bumps and contours and seasonal colours were once as familiar to me as the face I've shaved all the tumbling years since.

I'd built forts and tree houses on its vacant lands. I'd been intimate with the shapes and holes in its hedges and knew how to transit the yards of its lakefront properties unseen and without resort to the public road.

I'd known its shoreline with its attendant rocks and seawalls, its pocket beaches, boathouses, shallows and depths, its moored boats in summer and ice ridges in winter.

I'd known the lake the way I knew my own yard. I'd swum it, snorkelled it, paddled, rowed, waterskied, sailed, fished, and outboard- and inboard-motored it. I'd skated it and snow-mobiled it.

In all weathers and all seasons, I knew this place. It was part of me.

The town is Mariposa, where I was born. The street is Bay Street, where I grew up.

I know there are those who wish to forget their beginnings. There are others who couldn't give a damn about theirs, and still others who love theirs so much they wish they could return to them and never leave.

I am none of these.

I had a great family, great friends, great neighbours, great times—especially at Christmas—and I couldn't wait to go away to university and settle somewhere else.

For years, I was a Vancouver newspaper columnist who told the stories of the people in the cities and towns across Canada. But the best stories I know are from this town, from this street, and all of them somehow involve Christmas.

Time to tell these stories. You shouldn't sleepwalk through your life without acknowledging who and what makes life worth living.

As humourist Stephen Leacock—our most famous summer resident—once said so perfectly of his own sunshine sketches of this town, "If [this book] fails in its portrayal of the scenes and the country that it depicts, the fault lies rather with an art that is deficient than in an affection that is wanting."

So come, friends, let us away to the street and town that once we knew.

Welcome to Bay Street.

Welcome to Mariposa.

Angus and
the Skating Rink

THE TRAIL WHERE I parked near the end of my street was the upper of two trails that run parallel to one another. These trails didn't exist when I was a kid. They'd been railroad lines, separated by a boulevard of weeds and a tiny variation in elevation and corporate ownership. The upper line was the Canadian Pacific Railway route, the lower built by the old Grand Trunk Railroad but operated by Canadian National. In my day, both lines were still in sporadic use, but they've since been abandoned and converted by the municipality into trails—the CP line paved for bicyclists, the CN line a dirt trail that does for mere walkers.

The rail lines were once useful to me as places to leave pennies for the slow freights to flatten into thin, oval-shaped copper sheets. The culverts allowed us to play pooh sticks when we were very young, dropping twigs in the stream on the upper side and racing over to the other side to see whose stick would emerge first. All gone now. The forest that had been above the rail lines has been fully replaced by housing from a subdivision that has worked its way down the slope over the decades.

The gap between the two tracks, formerly milkweed and the occasional patch of bulrush and cattail, is now a dense mass of fern, sumac, and small trees. I was looking at this heavy growth, comparing it to what it used to be, when I was struck by what was missing.

The milkweed. Acres of it. All gone. Which meant the monarch butterflies were probably gone, too. In August, the air here used to be full of them and ... geez, where was the tiny house? There used to be a tiny house right where I was standing. A tiny house adored by the monarchs.

Angus's house.

Long before my time, in a slot by the old rail lines, a shingled railway shack housed a jigger the maintenance crews would push onto the tracks, then pleasantly while away the day putt-putting past the semaphores and switches. I thought those railway crews were the luckiest people on earth. Lords of their kingdom, they motored along the rails, occasionally deigning to stop and descend to earth to replace a rail here or a wooden tie there, men so superbly trained and attuned to their craft that they could clear the sticks and twigs from a clogged culvert in a matter of mere days, although a week or two might be needed to do the job properly. Theirs was a profession supremely worthy of a boy's worship on a summer afternoon. Gone now, as is their former shack that, at some point in the distant past, had been transformed into a tiny one-room dwelling, its wooden shingles painted railway rust red with an outhouse to match.

The man who converted it, and who lived there when I was growing up, was an old stick of a fellow every bit as dour and dilapidated as his domicile. His name was Angus. If anybody knew his last name, they kept it to themselves. He was just Angus.

Local lore had it that Angus had come down from Kapuskasing in northern Ontario as a young man in the 1920s. When and why he took over the little railway building—or what arrangements he made to occupy it—were lost to time. What was known was that he was a seasonal man.

In the spring, when the suckers were running in the nearby streams, he caught and sold them for fertilizer at five cents apiece to the local Co-op mill. In summer, he worked at the little lumber mill on Cedar Island, just down the line past the train station. He took the month of August off to be with his butterflies, but come September he'd put in a few shifts at the junkyard, also down the line past the train station. In winter, he built and maintained his rink.

Oh, that bit about his butterflies? It had to do with the milkweed around Angus's shack. For some reason, milkweed adored the locale, spreading south between the tracks and across the open fields as if a planted plantation. Nothing attracts monarch butterflies like a large patch of milkweed.

When I was growing up, little was known about the monarchs beyond the basics. They laid their eggs under milkweed leaves, their caterpillars ate the milkweed—making them toxic to birds—and they then formed chrysalises from which they'd emerge as orange-and-black-with-white-spots showstoppers. Then they'd all disappear and no one knew where.

I always wondered where they went. Apparently, so did an Ontario kid named Fred Urquhart. Urquhart graduated from the University of Toronto, then studied and followed the monarchs from 1937 until 1975. He discovered—in company with his wife, Nora—that in one epic flight, all the monarchs from southern Ontario flew to a tiny acre or two in Michoacán state in Mexico, a locale the butterflies had never seen but which was the exact spot from where their great-grandparents had set off the year before. Wondrous! It's also pleasing that the Spanish zoological term for butterfly is *mariposa*, and that the summer monarchs in Mariposa take off and fly to what is now a World Heritage Site called Reserva de Biosfera de la Mariposa Monarca.

But when I was young, and while the monarchs were still pumping up their wings and learning to fly and drink nectar and waiting for the urge to suddenly up and flutter across the continent, they'd hang around Angus's shack in such numbers that the kids at the YMCA day camp and the local summer school and assorted denizens of the old folks homes and nature clubs would charter buses to come and see Angus amid his butterflies. Angus being Angus, he'd put out rough-hewn benches so all would have a place to set a spell. It was rather wonderful, the very young and the very old coming together to set a spell under splendid summer skies in shared admiration of pattering swarms of monarch butterflies.

My parents first took me along to the shack one summer round about sunset, so that my first memory of Angus is of a wizened man dressed in overalls, backlit by an orange sun, surrounded by a halo of fluttering fire.

The monarchs, however, are not Angus's claim to Mariposa fame. That was just Angus in summer. It's Angus in winter that's legend, and that's because for as long as anyone can remember, Angus was the builder and keeper of the best little skating rink you ever saw.

Every Saturday and Sunday morning in winter—and each Christmas and Boxing Day, too—Angus would rise at three thirty and dress for the cold. He'd put on long underwear, three shirts, and overalls and stuff his boots with newspapers. He'd put on his thin and threadbare overcoat and tie the wrists with twine to deny the wind entrance. He'd pull on a garish orange-and-black toque, pick up a cloth string bag and sling it over his shoulder, grab his snow shovel and a comically large wrench, and go out into the dark.

He'd been doing this for decades.

He'd turn off Side Road onto Bay Street, walk about a hundred feet, and then veer off down a snow-covered trail—an undeveloped road allowance—and walk through the woods to the lake. Near the end of the trail above the lake was a large and sturdy municipal works cabinet, and next to that was a fire hydrant erected in anticipation of housing that had yet to materialize. Angus would leave his wrench on top of the cabinet, pick his way down the bank to the lake, and walk out to his rink.

Once the lake had frozen and could bear weight, and after it received its first snowfall, Angus fashioned a rink a short distance from the shore. For the duration of the winter, he arrived in the dark on weekends and holidays to shovel off his rink. It could take anywhere from thirty minutes to four hours, depending on the snow and wind drifts. He fashioned benches out of the rinkside snowbanks, topping them with wooden slats. When he was done, he went back to shore to ferry out the lengths of fire hose stashed in the works cabinet, hook the completed length up to the hydrant, then use the oversized wrench to crank the hydrant open. With a fireman's nozzle, he'd expertly direct a fine spray over the rink's surface to create a smooth and fast-freezing glass surface. When he was done, sometimes sweaty and shaking, Angus would seat himself rinkside on an old newspaper, pour himself a cup of coffee from a thermos in his string bag, and settle in to await what the day might bring.

Young boys were always first. Up with the sun, they'd be dropped off on Bay Street or would trek along the shoreline to the rink where they'd lace up their skates and don bits of hockey gear and swoop around the ice, batting pucks with oversized sticks, jabbering and calling to one another like gulls.

Then came even younger boys and the occasional girl, engulfed in snowsuits and scarves and toques, accompanied by parents who would heroically struggle to fit the children into their skates and then watch patiently as they not so much skated as walked around the rink on their ankles. These kids were invariably accompanied by dogs—happy dogs that barked and wagged their tails and followed their young masters wherever they tottered, anxious to take part in what seemed desperately exciting action. One dog, old and grey, was above such canine rapture and would make his way to Angus and lie down on the newspaper that Angus provided. Man and dog seemed content, asking nothing, and receiving exactly that.

When the sun was well up, the young girls came. In pretty wool hats and matching mittens and bright winter coats, their short precise straightforward skating motion and their white figure skates in sharp contrast to the scrambling, legs-everywhere, dogs-underfoot activities of the boys.

Somewhere around noon, Angus cleared the ice of its build-up of blade snow and ice chips, often applying another round of quick-freezing spray.

In the afternoon, a new crowd would move in—teenagers. Young men with bare heads and red cheeks who skated solo or in small groups, showing off for the young women. The young women seemed content to skate in packs, talking all the time and pretending to have trouble standing until a young man asked one of them for a skate and the girl would be transformed, able to hold hands and keep up as the two eddied their way round and around the perimeter of the rink in a seasonal dance as old as the country and as new as young love.

Here and there were scattered a middle-aged couple or two who—arm in arm—circled the ice with matched motions, gliding together like mated swans, all domestic trouble and strife evaporated in the sun and air and activity.

The skating continued all day, a merry-go-round of swirling colour and form in front of an old man who sat silently on his seat until the sun had gone.

When the last skater—usually one of the small boys—retired to the supper table, Angus struggled to his feet and stood stiffly. He would make sure the hose was stowed away and that he had his thermos and his shovel. Sometimes he picked something out of his string bag and looked at it before returning it to the bag. He trudged back the way he came to his little domicile between the tracks.

One special year, the skating on Angus's rink continued after dark. This was thanks to our lakefront neighbour J.W. Park, who operated the town's largest car dealership and was subject to sudden enthusiasms. Early that particular winter, J.W. and wife had enjoyed a Saturday skate on Angus's rink and later, at the dinner table, his wife foolishly remarked how nice it would be to have lights in order to have night skating on the lake.

It was well known in the neighbourhood that there were times when a remark could wander into J.W.'s head and bog down, often for days. His wife's innocent comment was obviously still stuck in there the next day because J.W. walked down the lake to the rink, sat himself next to Angus, and began to speak excitedly into Angus's ear. Angus listened, although he had no choice in the matter. He made no comment beyond a slight tilt of his head to indicate he was listening. J.W. rose, clapped Angus on the back, and hurried away.

Nobody noticed when J.W. sent a load of his mechanics down the trail that week, hauling equipment and material. Nobody knew anything until the next Saturday, when it was quickly noticed that someone had drilled holes through the ice around Angus's rink, stuck poles in them, and strung lights all around that connected to an array of car batteries.

"You just wait until seven tonight," J.W. said. "Bring your skates."

The kids were beside themselves with excitement, which meant their parents would have to forgo Sgt. Bilko that night in order to ferry their offspring down to the rink by seven o'clock sharp.

There were more than a hundred people clustered on and around the rink when, without any fanfare, J.W. flipped a switch and the rink was bathed in soft coloured lights.

It was magical, like something you'd see in a movie, the world a glorious winter's night where everyone skated, everyone talked, and everyone wanted to help clean the ice. Angus simply sat, as passive and benign as ever.

Over the next two weekends hundreds flocked to the rink to skate beneath the lights. And no wonder! Viewed from our house, looking down a half mile of the lake to the rink, it was a dollhouse scene, with tiny whirling windup figures, a patch of colour in the middle of darkness.

Everybody agreed it was perfect. And it was, until politics arrived in the form of Mayor Wilbur Campbell.

You'd have to have some sympathy for Mayor Campbell. He'd been mayor forever and assumed the world would remain the same forever. But he'd heard that J.W. Park was considering a run for mayor in the next year's election, and here was J.W. helping to create this wonderful and popular thing at a time when the mayor himself was thinking of championing a municipal outdoor rink at the waterfront park. To the mayor, it looked an awful lot like this car dealer was stealing what should have been the mayor's personal thunder, and all the while coveting Campbell's rightful position atop the town's municipal structure.

This was not a natural state of things. It could not be borne. It must be corrected.

Which is why the mayor was sorry to inform council at its next meeting that while he applauded and appreciated the efforts of Mariposa's private citizenry to contribute to a skating rink on the public's own beloved lake—"upon whose waters the immortal Samuel de Champlain once trod"—the simple fact of it was that these Bay Streeters were trespassing on a municipal road easement—an easement that the municipality had created and paid for and wished to retain in pristine condition—and, what's more, these people were stealing public materials from a public utility—that is, taking municipal water from a municipal hydrant with neither permission nor payment—to further benefit their well-to-do neighbourhood.

"It pains me to say it," the mayor said, and you could see how pained it made him to say it—sorrowful, even—because his brow was furrowed and his voice was lowered to the level he used when speaking at a funeral, "but we simply can't have the well-to-do taking precious municipal resources for the betterment of their own neighbourhood without payment or say-so, not when so many other deserving portions of this hard-working community, and so many other deserving Mariposa citizens—many of them, through no fault of their own, in situations of reduced circumstance—are doing without services that are already present in abundance on Bay Street."

"Bloody Campbell," J.W. groused to my father the next day. "His clan was first over Hadrian's Wall to loot, and now he wants to shut down a free rink on the lake because somebody other than a Campbell thought of it first."

"Well," my father said, "the rink is actually Angus's. There's no rink for anyone without Angus—and by the way, the Campbells weren't associated with looting after the Romans abandoned the wall—but I take your point."

My father thought for a moment, then asked J.W. if the YMCA hockey league's fundraising dinner—with its guest speaker—was set for next Sunday.

"It is," said J.W.

"Perfect," said my father. Noticing my presence, he said, "Step into the den, J.W. I've got an idea." They moved into my father's den and closed the door.

Five minutes later, the door flew open and J.W., a big grin on his face, barged across the living room and down the hallway and out the front door with only a "This'll work!" shouted over his shoulder to mark his exit.

My dad didn't say anything, not until the following Sunday morning when he suggested we might all want to be at Angus's rink around eight that night.

Apparently, a lot of people felt the need to be at Angus's rink that night, because when we arrived hundreds were milling around under the lights. Getting there proved to be remarkably easy. Someone from J.W.'s car dealership had taken the dealership's snowplough and run it back and forth all afternoon to create a snow road on the ice between Mariposa Beach Park and Angus's rink.

Just after eight, we could see a lot of flashing lights approaching along the lake.

It was a little parade.

Leading the way was a police car, its lights flashing. Inside the police car were the chief of police, two RCMP officers in red serge, and the little owl-faced man who was president of the YMCA hockey program. Right behind was the town's new fire truck, its own lights flashing and siren sounding. Hanging off the hoses and railings were the young stars of Mariposa's various hockey leagues—atom, squirt, peewee, bantam, midget, all of them. Bringing up the rear was a Cadillac convertible, top down, driven by a smiling J.W. Park and accompanied in the front seat by the newspaper's chief photographer.

In the back seat, wearing his trademark sheepish smile, sat Gordie Howe and his wife, Colleen.

Gordie—always willing to promote the sport of hockey— had been the special speaker at the YMCA's fundraiser dinner earlier in the evening, squeezing in the Mariposa appearance after the Red Wings game in Montreal on Saturday and their match against Toronto on Tuesday.

Did I mention that J.W. was on the board of the YMCA? Or that the chief of police was the chairman of the YMCA hockey league? Or that the fire chief's hockey-playing son was being honoured at the benefit dinner?

The greatest hockey player in the world mingled with the people, signed autographs, and responded to gushing compliments with his aw-shucks smile. He accepted the use of a pair of skates—which, as luck would have it, happened to be just his size and happened to be in the police car courtesy of the local sporting goods store owner who would later donate the autographed skates to the YMCA, which in turn would raffle them off and net a sizeable amount for the YMCA league development fund, which just happened to be the point of the benefit dinner in the first place—and Gordie laced them up and played a little shinny with the town's best young hockey players, who, providentially, had brought their skates and sticks with them on the fire truck. It all made for some great photos for the newspaper photographer, what with Gordie playing a pickup game with the kids and all. Did I mention my father was the editor and publisher of the local newspaper, the *Mariposa Daily Packet & Times*?

Gordie said a few nice words that were hard to make out because of his soft voice but were generally understood to imply that it was little outdoor rinks like this one that birthed Canada's great winter sport, and Canada's love affair with hockey, and how these rinks gave an outlet for boys—"And girls!" Colleen piped up—to grow up strong and healthy with the opportunity to create friendships, fellowship, and good sportsmanship.

"You have a beautiful little rink here," he concluded. "You're a lucky town."

While taking off his skates, Gordie leaned over to Angus and said a few words to him that we couldn't hear before shaking his hand.

Gordie and Colleen made their way back to the car, J.W. put the top up, and the little convoy moved off, its flashing lights visible all the way back to the park where, unseen by us, the fire truck peeled off and J.W.'s car was given a police escort all the way to the Howe's hotel in Toronto.

Angus was asked what the great Gordie Howe had said to him. Angus said nothing. He did, however, in what was seen as a burst of emotion, nod his head.

My mother, by dint of some sterling elbow work, happened to be standing right behind them during their brief encounter—did I mention my mother was a newspaper reporter before she met my father?—and was able to report that Gordie told Angus it was an honour to enjoy Angus's wonderful rink and he appreciated Angus's dedication to youth and to the community.

All of which you could have read about in Monday's newspaper, with its front-page picture of Gordie playing hockey with the kids—"World's greatest player takes a shift on Mariposa rink"—and an equally large picture on the Local News page with Gordie pretending to elbow young award winners at the YMCA banquet—"Gordie shows 'em Howe"—and still another on the Features page, right next to the Women's page, a picture of Gordie and Colleen—captured in a camera flash—skating arm and arm in perfect unison.

Days later, the paper received a mailed note from Mr. Howe thanking it for the photos, especially the one of him and Colleen. "That one means a lot to me," he wrote. "She makes me look good."

Mayor Campbell had been shut down, and he knew it.

J.W. didn't run against the mayor in the next election, having decided that municipal council required too much time away from "what's really important to me." Mariposa appreciated J.W.'s position. It was pretty much understood that what was really important to J.W. was fun, and that there was precious little of that commodity to be found within municipal chambers.

The rink lights, by the way, only lasted the one season, as J.W. moved on to more vital interests. Angus was back to running his rink in daylight hours only. He kept it up for a few more years, but eventually his strength left him and he couldn't do it any more.

In what turned out to be the last year of the rink, and having helped him—at my father's request—to tidy up and stow the fire hose at the end of the last day before Christmas, I found myself next to him as he opened his string bag to put away his thermos. In the bag, I saw a small framed picture.

I spoke up, saying I hoped he didn't mind my asking, but what was the picture? Why did he carry it with him to the rink?

Angus paused, as if thinking, then reached into his bag and pulled out *two* small framed photographs.

One was a young man and young woman dressed in winter clothes. They wore skates. They were holding hands.

The other was of a young woman. It was an oval cameo of a type popular many years ago, and the face—with its soft smile framed by curls of brown hair—radiated kindness. If you moved the picture, her eyes seemed to follow you in the nicest and gentlest of ways.

If I found the photos surprising, it paled to what came next. Angus spoke.

"The girl's Meg Galloway," he said. "Pretty little thing, ain't she? Prettiest thing I ever saw. Prettiest thing I'll ever see."

I didn't say anything. I just kept looking at her picture.

"Meg and me was sweethearts. 'Course, this was a long time ago. I remember how's we used to go down to the little

Common—where the Legion is now, you know?—and hold hands in the summer. Used to drink lemonade on her daddy's porch, up the hill on Side Street. All the things you used to do.

"But most of all, I remember we used to come down the street in winter time from her house and go through the woods to the lake and we'd skate.

"I was a good skater. Learned on the rivers where my daddy—gone now, bless him!—used to work in the mills. He'd give me a chair—I was no more than three or four—and I'd push the damn thing around on the ice from sun-up to sundown. My feet used to freeze, my hands'd be numb and red and my ankles real sore, but I'd push that old chair around all day and be back again the next, rarin' for more."

"What happened?" I asked, finding my voice.

"Well, we didn't have no money to get married so mostly we held hands and skated. Back when I was young, I used to take a hockey stick and stickhandle for miles when the river'd first freeze. Had a dog then. Me and the dog, we'd skate and go everywhere and pretend we was flying. We flew just about everywhere. We was young then."

And Meg?

"Meg and me, we'd go skating. Guess we was the best skaters around, specially when the lake'd first freeze. We didn't say much. We'd just skate and skate and never seem to get tired. Something about doing something you like with someone you like, you know? Neither of us minded, it being so much fun and all. We didn't need much and didn't ask for more. We was a fine pair. Then..."

I waited.

"One day—it was real cold that year—Meg came down with some bug or other. Don't know what it was. It went straight to her lungs and she got real weak. I went to see her—it was Christmas Day, I remember—and the doc told me how it didn't look good and that I shouldn't take no notice of what she was saying on account of how she was talking funny.

"When I went in to see her, Meg said she'd like to go skating. I said the lake was snowed under and we couldn't skate and she should get some rest. She said—and I remember this real well—she said, could I clear her a rink so's we could maybe go for a little skate?

"Well, she looked so beautiful and pale, and I thought I might as well be shovelling snow as sitting around her house, so I came down and cleared a rink. Right here. Right where we're sitting."

When Angus returned to the house, the doctor refused to allow him in. "See, Meg wasn't there any more."

Something small and supple in Angus's mind stiffened and snapped that day. He took it in his head that he must always keep a rink on the lake for people to skate on. It didn't make sense, but he never wavered.

"See, Meg whispered to me something no one else heard. She said we'd always be skating, me and her, and if I was to slip down to the lake, she'd meet me here and we'd have ourselves a skate.

"That's why I keep the rink every year."

There was a long pause.

"People think I'm some kind of old nut, clearing a rink, sitting in the snow. But see, I'm not watching the people skate. Not watching them at all. I'm skating too, see."

Angus died the following summer. There must have been some kind of church service or something for him, but I don't know. He wasn't part of the official fabric of Mariposa. He was cremated, which seemed unusual to me at the time. Afterward, it was J.W. Park who gathered some of us from the neighbourhood together at Angus's little place by the tracks with the odd request that we each bring a skate. My father and I came, each with a skate. The monarchs had emerged and were everywhere.

J.W. had a pot, and in the pot were Angus's ashes. He poured a little ash into each of our skates. On cue, we waved them in the air and the breeze took the ashes away.

I don't know what anyone else was thinking but I had an image of a young man and young woman arm in arm, skating, flying down a river of glass. Pretty sure nobody else had that image, not with all the monarchs around, but the monarchs didn't seem to notice what we were doing or mind us in any way.

Next day, they all disappeared.

Mrs. Torrance
and the Fireworks

THE OLD MUNICIPAL easement that was Angus's trail is now a paved entrance to a cul-de-sac adorned with well-to-do homes. One of them, an architectural tour de force, was built before I left Mariposa and was the home of a man believed by the boys of the town—check that, believed by the *men* of the town—to be the walking embodiment of sophisticated hedonism, the man we all wished we could be.

Sam Donnigan was an Ontario-born artist who illustrated stories for a variety of Canadian and American publications but who made the big time—and the big money—when he became a regular contributor of cartoons to a famous publication. Oh, he had two comic strips of his own in newspapers, and his illustrative art graced the pages of books, family magazines, and newspaper supplements, but what made his reputation were his cartoons in *Playboy*. Every month, every issue, there was a Sam Donnigan cartoon.

Playboy! Can you imagine? Oh man, oh man, oh man, he must be the wildest cat around, right? What a life he must lead! So Big City! So shaken, not stirred! His house must be Orgy Central! Mariposa boys were always on the lookout for the guy—someone with the open shirt and the gold chains and the fast car that would surely adorn a *Playboy* cartoonist—but potential sightings inevitably turned out to be a Toronto stockbroker or a travelling pool salesman. Meanwhile, a mild married man—pleasant, community-minded, and prone to tweeds—walked unseen among them, choosing to spend his wild nights in his upstairs studio churning out commercial artwork.

The properties in the cul-de-sac were on land formerly part of the Bayside estate, hived off between the wars as a residential development that failed to materialize, undeveloped and dormant for decades. Standing on the cul-de-sac now, you can see the original Bayside mansion perched on a slight rise, not as big as it once looked but still commanding the tremendous view over rolling lawns that cascade down to the lake.

This had been the home of Mrs. W.H. Torrance. It was a mansion I knew something about.

Interesting women were never rare on the ground in Mariposa. There was Mrs. Jayson, the wife of the local Presbyterian minister, who ran off with the famous Hollywood actor. There was Miss Pilliard, the tee-totalling librarian nobody noticed until the police arrived from the city and arrested her as the brains behind the notorious Martini Glass Bank Gang, so named for its trademark of leaving a martini glass on the counter during their robberies. (Police found witnesses stared at the glass throughout the robbery instead of directing their attention to the robbers.)

There were lesser extremes, such as Miss Jory, who never ventured beyond Mariposa and liked hats so much—"they make me feel happy and adventurous"—that she adorned her walls with hundreds of them, or Miss Dalby, who read tea leaves and drank scotch.

Interesting women? I should say so, but none more interesting than Mrs. W.H. Torrance, a woman who loved light but kept her drapes closed all day long. Of itself, not a remarkable or defining characteristic of eccentricity, but she had one trait that set her overwhelmingly apart in Mariposa. She was rich.

The town's largest house was built during the Depression for a timber baron who believed—wrongly, as it turned out—that our town would become the Canadian version of Newport, Rhode Island. Accordingly, his house wasn't just big by our standards, it was big by anyone's standards. Designed by the architect of Toronto's Casa Loma, it was a two-storey stone chateau, with a courtyard and wings and French doors and fantastic dormer windows and multiple chimneys set amid steep slate roofs. One week after it was completed, and before he ever set foot in it, the timber baron died.

Bayside, as the realtors called it, was put up for sale and stood empty until—on the day of the first thousand-bomber raid on Berlin—it was sold to a Mr. and Mrs. W.H. Torrance. Naturally, everyone in town was interested in who would want to buy it and, every bit as important, who was wealthy enough to buy it. It was a nice diversion for a town weary of losing its children to the war.

Interest didn't exactly die down when two truckloads of carpenters, masons, and painters arrived from the city and set to work on the house. The artisans lived in large tents on the property and were serviced by their own cook in a cook tent, and every one of them was Portuguese. Literally nobody on the work site spoke English, which is why Maria, wife of Carl the baker, was dispatched to Bayside to investigate, returning with the news that the men were hired to redo the interior to precise specifications—real blueprints were involved!—and they were required to live, eat, and sleep on the grounds. The workers were paid handsomely for their efforts, and for their silence. A rumour went round to the effect that there was no Mr. and Mrs. W.H. Torrance, that the government had bought the estate and was turning it into some kind of centre for secret projects, but no one could think of how renovating a huge estate house in Mariposa could be part of the secret war effort.

Eventually the workmen moved on and a dapper grey-haired little man named Bill—"Just Bill," he said, "That's the name I go by"—moved into the little apartment over the garages and began work on the flowerbeds. Two weeks later, a long dark touring car drove through town and up to the Bayside gates, and in.

Mrs. W.H. Torrance had arrived.

Townsfolk performed prodigies of detective work but learned only that Mrs. Torrance was alone, with no sign of a Mr. W.H. Torrance, and that she kept three maids on three-day rotations, each driven up from the city then back again in the big touring car.

Despite always having the drapes, blinds, and shutters drawn, lowered, or closed, Mrs. Torrance was not a recluse. It just suited the town, because of her wealth, to see her as one. Yes, she wore dark glasses wherever she went—shopping, for instance, or to Sunday services at the Anglican church where her offering plate contributions practically paid for a new font—but this was written off as eyewear appropriate to her station, i.e., a wealthy eccentric. Mrs. Torrance herself was unfailingly polite, courteous, and pleasant in her conversations. She never put on airs. The only blemish anyone could apply was her maddening failure to provide any hint of her life before Mariposa.

Once the town understood Mrs. Torrance meant to stay in Mariposa, she was accepted. It didn't mean people lost interest in her; it only meant that as a local, she was one of us, and it didn't do to snoop into a neighbour's affairs. You could do that with outsiders but not with your neighbours.

Which is where matters stood for years until the time came when Mrs. Torrance grew ill. She was seen less and less around town. Rumours circulated that she had cancer, but as always with Mrs. Torrance, nobody seemed to know anything. The only person outside the estate who did know something was the young boy who was her newspaper carrier.

Me.

In the days before subscribers paid the newspaper directly, newspaper boys and girls would knock on their customers' doors each week to collect the week's subscription fee. Carriers got to step inside and see how the subscriber lived, what they ate, and how they were fixed for ready cash as they rooted through wallets and purses and the occasional chesterfield—sometimes, a piggy bank was raided—for the coins to pay the small weekly subscription.

My paper route was a long portion of North Street—which ran east and west, naturally—and all of Bay Street. I had wanted to be a *Toronto Star* or *Toronto Telegram* carrier—much more lucrative for a carrier—but my father, as publisher of the *Mariposa Daily Packet & Times*, wasn't having any of it. Either a boy properly delivered the local news and the wares of local advertisers or nothing at all. None of your big-city heresies for a growing Mariposa boy. My father never said any of this of course, but it was understood through a kind of family osmosis that it would be a blow to him if I delivered anything but the *Packet*.

The last stop on my newspaper route was Bayside. I delivered the newspaper to the big house, but on Fridays—the day I collected—I would knock on the door of Bill's apartment over the garage, as he was the one who paid Bayside's delivery bills. Bill was always prompt, the money in an envelope ready for pick up. We got into the habit of sitting down and I'd have a ginger ale and he'd have a brandy with his pipe and we'd pass a few pleasant moments discussing this or that.

He liked to talk and I liked to listen. He spoke of gardening, of which I knew nothing, and of world events, of which I knew very little, and of history, of which I was beginning to learn a lot. In summer, we'd sit on the outside bench and watch the lowering sun change the colour of the lake. In winter, when it was dark early, we'd sit at his kitchen table in quarters done up as an English cottage with whitewashed walls, exposed roof beams, and a couple of hat racks over a fireplace.

I never asked him directly about Mrs. Torrance, but I did once ask him about himself. He said he'd been in business but that he loved gardening and preferred it to lesser endeavours like the insurance trade. He'd been married and had had a son. A fine boy. Killed early in the war. That was his picture on the fireplace. What was it like to work for Mrs. Torrance? Fine, he said. Nice woman. Very private. Rather alike in that respect, he said.

I told him everyone wondered about her and was interested in her and he laughed and said that was to be expected but that Mrs. Torrance simply liked her privacy.

I had the paper route for five years and it wasn't until what proved to be my final year as a carrier that the veil of Bayside lifted a little.

It was a snowy December evening during the time of the health rumours and I was walking up the long drive to deliver the last paper when the estate's work car—a Plymouth Valiant—appeared before me with Bill at the wheel. He stopped, rolled down the window, and said he was going to the station to meet the doctor off the evening train from the city.

"I want to ask a favour," he said. "While I'm fetching the doctor, I want you to go up and into the house, go along the main corridor to the staircase, up the stairs to the second floor, down the corridor to your right until you see a chair outside a room. That's Mrs. Torrance's room. She's asleep right now, but I want you to sit outside the room until I get back. There's a pill-box by the chair. If she wakes and asks for medication, you're to give her one pill. Only one. Got it? Right, off you go."

I ran to the kitchen door, wiped my feet vigorously on the mat, opened the thick wooden door, and stepped in, becoming one of the first locals to step inside Mrs. Torrance's Bayside.

I made my way down the corridor, up the grand staircase, then along to the room with the chair in front of it. The door was ajar. I sat down, fidgeted, tried to read the paper.

A voice called from the room.

"Bill?"

No, I explained. It was the paperboy. Bill had gone to get the doctor at the train station.

"Come in," said the voice. "Let's have a look at you."

I pushed the door open and went in.

As rooms go, it was really something. Enormous, with comfortable chairs and ottomans positioned here and there, and highly polished tables with vases of flowers. Thick grey velvet curtains covered the entire length of the wall in front of me. There was a handsome fireplace, floor-to-ceiling bookcases, and against the wall with the door—facing the curtains—was a very large bed. Propped up on pillows and a bolster was Mrs. Torrance. Grey-haired, grey-skinned, sans sunglasses.

"Haven't had many visitors here," she said.

I said I hoped she didn't mind this one. Was there anything I could get her?

"You interested in the sky?" she asked.

I said yes.

"Pretend you're hoisting a flag and pull that curtain cord in the corner. The moon will be up and it's a full one tonight."

I pulled. The curtains slid back to a reveal a series of complicated glass doors that could, in warmer weather, be unlatched and pushed along tracks to open the entire wall to the outdoors.

Mrs. Torrance clicked a switch by her bed, the lights went out, and the room was flooded with stark white moonlight reflected off the snowy lawns and frozen lake.

"I've always enjoyed light," she said. "That may seem odd given how dark I keep the house, but it's true. I love displays of light. Especially fireworks. As a girl, they were always my favourite. What I'd really enjoy, more than anything I can think of, is to see fireworks again. I'd love to see some lovely fireworks out this window. I'd love to be that girl again."

She closed her eyes. Her breathing was heavy but rhythmic. I looked around the room, admiring it in the harsh moonlight. A photograph on the mantle caught my eye. I tiptoed over to look at it, then tiptoed out into the corridor and waited until Bill and the doctor showed up.

Bill and I sat in the kitchen and I told him what Mrs. Torrance had said about fireworks. He looked thoughtful. "Maybe it can be arranged," he said.

Next day, Bill walked down our driveway and spoke with my father. They went into the den, and when my father came out, it was to make a series of phone calls. Within an hour, my mother was making coffee for a half dozen men in the living room who were listening to Mr. Lewis, Mariposa's town clerk. In those days, a town clerk was underpaid, overworked, underappreciated, and usually the smartest man in any room.

"To sum up," he said, "we are agreed. Bill, here, wishes to stage a fireworks display on the lands of his employer on Christmas Eve, two weeks hence, and is happy to open the occasion to any and all members of the Mariposa public that might be interested. The fireworks display will be sufficiently large and powerful as to require a provincial license for the detonation of the necessary materials, but as the time frame is short, and the wheels of provincial procedure grind slow—and never so slow as the period before and after Christmas—it is therefore agreed that the province shall *not* be informed of the upcoming display. We will keep them in the dark. While this frees us in some regards, it restricts us in others."

Mr. Lewis was a terrific town clerk. He treated municipal councillors the way an elderly butler would treat a family's fractious backward child—with courtesy, kindness, and above all, firmness.

Seated around Mr. Lewis in the living room were Bill, my father, the fire chief—as the representative of public safety—the presidents of the chamber of commerce and Rotary and Kiwanis clubs—as representatives of civic-minded organizations ready to pitch in for community good works at a moment's notice and at no cost to the municipality—and J.W. Park, who wasn't going to miss out on anything involving gunpowder. As the owner of a car dealership, he was—as a matter of professional necessity—familiar with human nature, Man's predilection for aerial demonstrations of pyrotechnical artistry, and a lover of really loud bangs.

"There is the matter of liability and insurance," Mr. Lewis continued. "This is a private citizen's display of fireworks. We've agreed that the normal insurance taken out for a municipal fireworks display—insurance that is inexpensive for a municipality able to draw upon its own police, fire, and medical services—is too expensive for Bill's employer. For its part, the municipality itself can neither host, provide services for, nor pay for such an event without provincial approval.

"Now, the municipality *could* do it all under the table, but there would still be a record in the in-camera minutes, so that won't work. However, the president of the Chamber of Commerce assures us that the Chamber qualifies for the same preferential insurance rate, and thus could indemnify the event without the necessity of recording the financial outlay in any of its minutes or documents. Correct?"

The president of the Mariposa Chamber of Commerce nodded his head.

"Therefore," Mr. Lewis continued, "Bill will provide a contribution to the Chamber in the form of a cheque equal to the amount of the insurance. For its part, the Chamber will—with no written, recorded, or in any way public reason or rationale— agree to insure a fireworks display on property thoughtfully donated by Mrs. Torrance. Agreed?"

Everyone nodded.

"Further," Mr. Lewis continued, "Rotary and Kiwanis will turn out their memberships to help service and secure the event and ensure the site is clean and safe before and after the event."

"We'll rope in the Lions and Kinsmen, too," said the Rotary Club president. "They're young. They have better backs and more energy for this sort of thing."

"Fine," Mr. Lewis said. "I'll direct the ambulance to be there—the attendants can book off at Mrs. Torrance's address for their dinner break, thereby solving the matter of their duty logs and timesheets—and the chief here will have the fire truck stationed on site under the guise of conducting winter fire practice. It's highly unlikely that any wayward spark will find something to ignite, it being winter, but the insurers must be satisfied."

Everyone nodded again.

"This brings me to my last point," Mr. Lewis said. "The lake and its ice."

He paused for effect.

"While the ice is certainly thick enough this year to bear the weight of many people, I confess to a certain ignorance concerning the properties of lake ice under the influence of multiple persons congregating upon it. Is it possible that the ice might sag, or crack, or even break open under the unknown weight of an unknown assemblage of people?"

"Leave it to me," said J.W. He went to the phone and called Mr. Cunningham, the retired high school science teacher. We heard him ask Mr. Cunningham what would happen if you got together a few people—one or two thousand of them, say—in one spot on the lake in December. J.W. listened politely for several minutes, thanked Mr. Cunningham, hung up, and returned to his chair.

"There's apparently much to consider," J.W. said. "The pound pressure per square inch and various coefficients and stress points and such, but the nut of it is, it'll be just fine. But we'll keep the old folks on the shore, just to be safe. The kids can sit or stand out on the ice."

There was a moment of silence as the room struggled to follow his logic. J.W. took no offence and explained his reasoning.

"Your basic senior wears a lot of sweaters and coats and uses canes and crutches and probably couldn't swim if she had to, whereas your basic youngster is light and buoyant and not freighted by layers of clothing. It only makes sense."

Mr. Lewis paused, as if he weren't entirely convinced by J.W.'s sanguine beliefs, but as I said, he was a good municipal clerk and accustomed to having to look the other way from time to time in order to satisfy the enthusiasms of the few for the greater benefit of the many.

"One last thing," Mr. Lewis said. "Bill has said the public is welcome, but to keep the province out of it, there can be no formal invitation to the public. Any public mention would, whether through the newspaper or radio or advertising handbill, eventually come to the attention of the province. We want people to know about the fireworks, but we can't publicly inform them about it. Gentleman, any ideas?"

Nobody had a workable answer.

Except Mr. Lewis. Turns out he knew exactly what to do all along, which was to rise and go to the phone, make a little production of looking up a number in the phone book although he obviously knew the number by heart, dial it, and lower his voice to the level he used when explaining a complicated infrastructure funding situation to a somnambulant and barely sentient council, before hanging up and returning with a small smile on his face.

"That was the widow, Miss Josie Braillie," he said. "I told her about the fireworks display on Christmas Eve—set to start at 7 PM sharp—and said it was a secret, just something set up as a family thing for Mrs. Torrance at her home, and that people should bring their own lawn chairs."

Brilliant! Miss Josie Braillie! Within ten days there wouldn't be anyone in Mariposa who didn't know about the private fireworks except the occasional shut-in or possibly a coma patient in the hospital's one-bed ICU.

Preparations went swimmingly. The Empire Fireworks Company from Albany, New York, arrived and set up shop on the shoreline, building sand berms, anchoring mortars, and using terms likes "viewshed" and "exothermic chemical reaction" and "high-lift Mariah" and "black match" and "lift charge" that added immeasurably to a boy's growing vocabulary.

The only hiccup came from the churches. Christmas Eve was a Sunday that year and there was pastoral grumbling as to how these fireworks might lure weaker parishioners and lesser believers away from the Bethlehem manger, but a visit from Bill and Charlie Davidson—the latter being our likeable neighbour who attended services at all the major churches depending on what hymns they were planning to sing—plus Bill's deposit of an unexpected envelope on the offering tray quelled any religious uprisings. As Charlie told ministers and pastors and priests, fireworks at seven should set up the evening services and midnight mass rather nicely. Besides, he said, the Mariposa Silver Band would be on the shore, playing carols and seasonal musical works.

The town abuzz? I should say so. Fireworks! In winter! Nobody had heard of such a thing. And at the Torrance estate!

What was that all about? You could cut the speculation with a spoon.

And what about the ice? Would it hold? Townsfolk shivered with frissons of danger and entertained visions of people drawn down into inky depths under the ice. A sudden thaw a few days before the fireworks didn't calm any nerves, the snow melting and turning into mini lakes on top of the ice, but a deep cold spell turned the melt water into a hard and smooth surface for Christmas Eve. You might slip on it, but you wouldn't fall through it.

People began gathering on the lake and shore in front of Bayside in the late afternoon. Everyone seemed to bring their own chair and the crowd grew larger as the day grew darker. At 6:00, the Mariposa Silver Band began to play, and by 6:30, one or two thousand people were spread out in a fan in front of the great artificial sand beach created by the fireworks team.

At 6:45, a single aerial bomb erupted from a mortar with that distinctive firework launching sound—*whump!*—and exploded overhead. At 6:50, two aerial bombs shot out of mortars—*whump! whump!*—and detonated above. At 6:55, three aerial bombs exploded. At 6:59—we were all consulting watches now—the Mariposa Silver Band stopped playing and a great hush fell across the shore and lake.

At 7 sharp, there were five *whump*s from five mortars and five burning fuses could be seen rocketing upward and on and on and on until they disappeared from sight above, then five gigantic flashes and concussions shook the heavens and lit up the world. For a single second, you could see the high clouds, the sky, the smoke in the air, the mirrored lake, the people, the estate, all of it frozen in time.

Everyone gasped.

There was a pause, and just as you began to wonder if something had gone wrong and that was all there was, it began—the most intense and sustained twenty minutes of fireworks any-one had ever or would ever see.

Not just a solo peony effect here or a couple of chrysanthe-mums there, but *gardens* of them. Not just a few shooting stars and a handful of comets, but *galaxies* of them.

The only break in the action was for a set piece, a long line strung between poles on the shore which, when ignited, pro-duced the effect of a waterfall, pouring forth first in multiple colours, then in gold, and finally all in cascading silver, millions of falling sparks reflecting off people's glasses and the Mariposa Silver Band's polished instruments and the closed windows and doors of the mansion—with the exception of a wide bal-cony door on the second floor that was open to the night.

There were two oddities about the fireworks. The first was their height.

With few exceptions, these fireworks weren't shot off all that high in the sky. They were much lower than you might expect. Oh, high enough, to be sure, but you felt you could almost touch them.

I knew why.

I'd seen the open upper bedroom balcony door. The bed-room, I realized, was the viewshed. Everything was designed to be visible within its sight lines. You couldn't see really high effects from it, so you don't make any really high effects. Keep everything low and within the viewshed.

The other oddity was the ice, its silvered glass surface reflecting every degree of brightness and nuance of colour and somehow heightening it. You didn't even have to watch the fireworks in the heavens overhead. You could look down and see them exploding below your feet. Together, ice and sky bounced layers of colour and noise across the snow-covered grounds and the mansion and the trees, and from the shore it looked like a molten riot throbbing under the ice, erupting in ribbons that trailed off toward the centre of the dark lake.

A furious finale of colour and walloping concussions ended the performance. As the applause died away, the Mariposa Silver Band struck up "O Little Town of Bethlehem" and people gathered up their chairs and headed home to Christmas Eve.

I looked up. The upper balcony doors were closed now, the dark grey curtains drawn. I thought about the part of the carol that goes,

Yet in the dark street shineth
The everlasting light.
The hopes and fears of all the years
Are met in thee tonight.

I went home to stocking and eggnog and Christmas.

Mrs. Torrance died in January. Everyone agreed her passing was a pity, that she had been a nice woman, and that nobody ever did know anything about her, and who was going to buy Bayside?

Bill cancelled the estate's newspaper subscription and said he'd be leaving as the property was to be sold by a Toronto realtor on behalf of some kind of Torrance family trust. He thanked me for delivering the paper and for my help with the fireworks, and he said he enjoyed our Friday talks.

I said I enjoyed them, too, but could I ask him one question?

"Sure," he said.

I pointed to the house and asked, "Who was she?"

He smiled.

"She was," he said, "a wealthy woman who married her sweetheart and had a child, and when the child went away and died, she sort of went away, too.

"It's why she came here," he said. "After her boy died, she wanted to be left alone. I know she caused a lot of talk here, but her ways were harmless and whatever sins she might have had were small and easily forgiven. She had the money to do what she wanted, and she wanted to be alone, to be in charge, not have any more ties."

"Did that include her husband?" I asked.

"Why would you ask that?"

I told him I had seen the photograph on the mantle in her bedroom. It was a picture of Mrs. Torrance and a young man in an air force uniform. It was the same young uniformed man in the picture on Bill's mantle.

"The 'W' in W.H. Torrance stands for William, doesn't it?" I said.

"Well, you can just call me Bill," he said. "I wanted her to be happy, and if that meant she had to be alone, so be it. I'd be close by, indulging my taste for small living and gardening, keeping an eye on her. It was an odd arrangement, I know, but it suited us."

He thanked me again for the fireworks. He said it had been one of her happiest Christmases in years.

I left him there in his viewshed—a dapper little man in a little apartment over the garages of an empty estate on the Mariposa lakeshore—and never saw him again.

The Town Crier

BACK ON BAY Street, I walk up the little rise to where the street curves and begins its multi-block run down to a distant and unseen Mariposa Beach Park. The far side of the street where the milkweed held sway is suburban homes now, leafy and pleasant and inoffensive, indistinguishable from housing in any town in any province in the country. The gates of Bayside are visible on the water side of the street but the old garage that sat next to the estate entrance has been replaced by a grassy berm.

It shouldn't have surprised me the garage was gone—it was dilapidated and falling down when I knew it years ago—but for some reason it did. The garage had always been a mystery, standing alone throughout my childhood, out of character with the street, no one knowing who owned it or even what property it had originally belonged to, but it held special meaning for the neighbourhood kids. It was the winter hibernation cave of a Mariposa institution as familiar to our streets as popsicles, Lucky Elephant pink candy popcorn, and posters for summer dances at the Club Pavalon.

The garage had been the home of a 1957 white-and-sunburst-yellow Nash Metropolitan called the Town Crier, the central player in events that landed Mariposa on the front page of newspapers across North America.

It's a story that can be said to have had its beginning on a long-ago June day, when eleven-year-old Betty Jean Campbell flounced into her father's office above the hardware store and pronounced herself bored.

"It's hot," she said. "There's nothing to do. I wish it were Christmas. I wish we could have Christmas in summer."

Betty Jean was of an age easily bored, but she was—as all daughters are—the apple of her father's eye. And her father was Mayor Wilbur Campbell. The mayor was occupied with a sheaf of invoices for his hardware store, and although he'd been studying these invoices for an hour, he had yet to divine their meaning.

In truth, the mayor was bored, too. He did not particularly enjoy proprietorship of the hardware store because he found it, well, boring. He much preferred being mayor, a position he'd held for a long, long time and which, from time to time it must be admitted, he became bored with, too.

It was Wilbur Campbell's nature to become bored. From long experience, he knew he needed something—a project, say—to get his juices flowing, something that would excite the town, which in turn would excite him, which would send his family running for the safety of their rooms because, in their experience, an excited mayor usually preceded embarrassment for everyone.

Wilbur R. Campbell was like any publicity-seeking mayor, only more so. He was affable in public—a necessity for any elected official—with an eye ever out for the main chance. What set him apart from his municipal peers was what he considered an opportunity for glory and worthy of embrace, which was—in their eyes—freighted with risk of folly and failure and therefore to be avoided.

Mayor Campbell was not a common-sense mayor. Failure forever surprised him because he never considered it a possibility.

When he was upset with what he saw as Ottawa's casual dismissal of Mariposa's proposal to create a free-trade zone on the old municipal parking lot, he petitioned Ottawa instead to grant Mariposa free port status for its municipal wharf. This was an odd demand as Mariposa sits on a fresh-water lake, far from international borders, but it was standard operating procedure for the mayor. He often threatened to take the town out of Confederation, once going so far as to withdraw the town unilaterally, proclaiming Mariposa a constitutional monarchy with himself as elected prime minister, albeit with continued allegiance to the Queen under a new royal coat of arms that sported a corgi instead of a lion.

He was his own worst enemy, always.

One time, he put together a special day to draw investors and industrialists to Mariposa.

What value, he lectured council, were brochures and advertisements in extolling the virtues of a town when set against the prospect of big city industrialists and investors walking Main Street and fingering the fine retail wares on display, marvelling at the new swings and teeter-totters in the park, visiting the municipal generating plant north of town—the same power plant Campbell had tried to sell to make a few bucks for the town—where abundant power is generated and offered at attractive small-town rates to anyone who wanted to buy it. Why, just to smell the fresh air of Mariposa—though not in the south end, where the tannery was located—would make an industrialist feel alive and excited about setting up shop in such a glorious go-ahead place.

You had to give the mayor his due. The day was set, invitations extended, and through the mayor's extensive organizational efforts, activities were arranged and local hopes raised. When on the appointed day the industrialists and investors showed up from the city in droves, the mayor was ready for them.

Visitors admired the schools and playgrounds where workers' families might flourish. The power plant shone and hummed with power, its sluices burbling happily in the sunshine. The serviced and appropriately zoned plots of industrial land beckoned, awaiting only a sensible-yet-far-sighted investor's signature. Main Street retailers laid out their latest fashions, furniture, and hardware goods, and everywhere the sun shone down on the town's leafy streets and affordable housing.

Yet it was in the small things, things that had nothing directly to do with business and commerce, that the mayor showed off his superior skills

For those of a pious bent, and thus more likely to bring their wives, there were individual visits to appropriate churches, the local pastors and parsons alerted and standing ready to service a wealthy investor's higher spiritual needs. The Imperial Order of the Daughters of the Empire laid on lunches and historical tours. For those who had spent time in the military, the Legion was their host at a roast beef and complementary-glass-of-beer lunch. For golfers, it was luncheon at the clubhouse and a round at the nine-hole country club. Everyone was offered an excursion on the lake with tea and hot chocolate aboard the *Miss Mariposa*.

But it was for the fishermen that Campbell displayed his peculiar genius.

For the bass fishermen, he laid on Harold Bolland with his large open fishing boat and his encyclopaedic knowledge of the lake. Harold, it was said, knew every fish in the lake, or at least knew where they were resident at any given time of the year.

The mayor convinced town council to hire Harold's boat and gear and local knowledge for the afternoon with instructions to take his charges to where the large-mouth bass were biting. As a result, everyone on Harold's boat that afternoon—spirited off to an unmarked shoal west of Chief Island—landed a foot-long bass or larger, and were in a mood to look kindly on a town that could provide such an industrial investment experience.

The mayor also had council hire Jack Goodoar and his local piscine knowledge as personal guide for a single investor—a very large investor—whose passion was the pursuit of the mighty muskellunge, or muskie, the largest of the pike family. Jake really *was* on a first-name basis with the muskie that inhabited or transited through the gap—known as the Narrows— between our lake and the larger southern lake. Among the muskie were two long-time residents whom he called Nick and Nora, and they were local stars. Nick was a gargantuan seven-footer, and Nora clocked in at five feet. Big and incredibly dramatic in a fresh-water setting, you could sometimes see them swimming slowly through the shallows of the reed beds. They were also the most dimwitted fish imaginable, because someone in Jack's boat caught them pretty much on a weekly basis.

Jack told his charters that any muskie over three feet long had to be released, and although unused to the catch-and-release concept at the time, clients were so thrilled at the prospect of catching something larger than could be found in their aquarium that they always agreed.

The muskie would strike the lure, and Jack would tenderly remove the hook and release the fish—Nick or Nora, it didn't matter which—secure in the knowledge that nothing benefits a fishing guide's reputation so much as a trophy catch. Indeed, Nick and Nora appeared regularly in small newspapers around North America in photos submitted by proud holders of a record Ontario muskie, all of them unaware it was the same trophy caught over and over, year after year, in our little lake.

So it was that the big investor, accustomed to paying a fortune for guided experiences in northern Ontario and Manitoba and the Northwest Territories, was in the boat trolling and chewing on a cigar for a mere ten minutes before Nick hit the lure right on schedule and waited calmly to be lifted into the boat by willing hands, photographed in the company of the beaming industrialist, and then gently returned to the lake and the care and company of Nora.

Ready to invest? I should say so. All of them were. They felt good about themselves and about the little town. They said as much to one another as they gathered at town hall to receive a commemorative key chain and the final thanks of a community honoured to have hosted so many good and gifted visitors from the city.

And that's when the mayor, who had put the whole day together, showed up.

Nobody knows why anybody does anything, only that it is predictable that some people do some things differently because it's what they always do. Having crafted a perfect experience for investors and industrialists, Mayor Campbell, who had simply to say "Thank you" and "Hope to see you soon" to crown the day, instead did something different, something inexplicable, something predictably Campbellian.

For reasons known only to himself, the mayor—eschewing traditional business garb or symbols of office—showed up in front of the cameras and the industrialists and investors dressed in the Lincoln green of Robin Hood, complete with bow and quiver slung over his hooded shoulder, and instead of saying "Thank you" and "Hope to see you soon" announced to the cameras that he was prepared "to take from the rich and give to the poor local ratepayer."

Reaction was immediate and nicely subtle. The investors and industrialists didn't automatically stampede toward the door. That would have been the reaction of your small-time businessman or inexperienced rural investor. No, they simply looked at their watches and pursed their lips and said, "Say, is *that* the time?" and moved quickly and efficiently to the exits, never once cracking a wallet or pausing to sign a development agreement. The front page on the *Mariposa Daily Packet & Times* the next day showed the mayor running after a line of departing Cadillacs and Lincolns—bow unstrung and quiver abandoned on the ground behind him—with the caption, "Halt, varlets! I was only kidding!"

We understood. It was the mayor being the mayor. He couldn't help himself.

So when Betty Jean moped in to his office that June morning and unloaded her comment about Christmas in July, you could pretty much see the acetylene ignite in his head.

Christmas in summer? Christmas in July? Yes!

He dropped the invoices, grabbed his calendar, noted the annual Dominion Day softball tournament pencilled in on July 1—a major event in our town and thus a major event in the life of a local politician—slapped his thigh, and said to a supremely uninterested Betty Jean, "Honey, I've got it."

Within the hour, many others in Mariposa would also have it. Including my father, who chanced to answer the phone at home.

"Jimbo?" Campbell's voice boomed out of the earpiece. "I've got it. You're gonna love it."

My father was Jim to his friends, J.B. to anyone at the newspaper, and Mr. Lamb to everyone else. Only Mayor Campbell called him Jimbo, and as the newspaper publisher in Mariposa, he'd heard a few Jimbos sing out of receivers at work and at home.

"Christmas in July, Jimbo. It's perfect. We run the July 1 ball tourney with a Christmas theme. Set up booths for the merchants to flog Christmas presents, souvenir stuff. Good for the local economy. And the publicity, Jimbo! It's a long weekend, right? The city papers got nothing to run in their Monday editions but beach shots and fireworks. You don't think they won't leap at a photo of a bunch of Santas playing ball? It can't miss."

I recall my father saying the ball players might not think it such a great idea and that the tournament was pretty solid stuff without the Santa nonsense, but his objections were shunted aside. The mayor's mind had seized on the Christmas theme like a steel trap on a hapless animal and no way was it going to wriggle clear.

With the school year winding down and the prospect of a summer of swimming and boating and pickup ball games ahead, I was blissfully ignorant of adult organizational efforts to mount a Christmas offensive in July. There were overheard mutterings and oaths from among our parents but us kids paid it no more mind than the background buzzing of summer bees.

It was during the last week of June that the public got to hear about the big event. Bert Jones saw to that. Bert Jones drove the Town Crier.

Bert was a notorious lush who supported himself with an unusual array of jobs. During winter months, he tore tickets at the hockey rink. On nights when there was no hockey game or paid admission to figure skating or public skating, Bert donned a red jacket and black bowtie and tore tickets at the town's movie house, the Gaiety, where his cousin was the manager.

Once the tulips and blossoms were out, and the warm weather looked to stay, Bert would give his fingers a rest from tearing tickets and wander down to the garage he rented on Bay Street by the gates of Bayside, open the padlocked door, hook up a battery to the 1957 white-and-sunburst-yellow Nash Metropolitan inside, and fire it up.

It took a while, and there would be strange sounds emerging from the open garage door—sounds like stones shaken in a tin can by someone with emphysema—but soon enough Bert would be seen grinding gears on his three-on-the-tree transmission and putt-putting on barely inflated tires along Bay Street, the enormous loudspeaker on top of the car and its attendant mini-billboards wreathed in cobwebs and dust. Bert would lay down a haze of blue smoke all the way to his other cousin's garage for the Nash's annual tune-up and the start of his summer employment as the Town Crier.

For the next few months, the Nash would chug through neighbourhood after neighbourhood again and again as Bert's smoke-and-liquor voice inundated homeowners and pedestrians with announcements of coming events, dances, clothing sales, and farm auctions.

But on this late June morning, Bert had only one long message and it commanded our full attention.

Big, big, big holiday weekend!

Folks, it's Christmas in July this Saturday at the Mariposa Community Centre and Fairgrounds.

Come see Santa and his elves!

All-day softball tournament! Fireworks! Seasonal foods and beverages!

Religious pageantry! Enter your baby in the Baby Jesus lookalike contest!

Come see Canada's only officially sanctioned reindeer races!

The Three Wise Men will arrive bearing gifts by parachute!

World-renowned rocketeer Rocky Barnes will demonstrate his rocket backpack, as seen in the pages of Popular Mechanics!

Midget wrestling!

Shop and flop in the bleachers and then watch filming of CKCO's *top-rated* Tiny Tot Talent Time *with the biggest little kid himself, host Big Al Parker!*

Rides for the kiddies!

Yes, it's Christmas in July! It's the big, big, big holiday week-end . . . over and over and again and again through the daylight and twilight hours leading up to July 1, Dominion Day.

Even my father had to admit the event was the talk of the town. Certainly, it was all that my friends and I talked about on the last day of school. Never mind Santa. A rocket back-pack? Maybe one of the parachutes wouldn't open! What kid could resist?

Dominion Day dawned clear and cloudless, and with every prospect of being a July scorcher. From out of the neighbour-hood streets, even from the cottages down on the lake past Bayside, trickles of pedestrians and streams of family autos made their way toward the fairgrounds, where they foamed around the fairground gates.

Again, you had to give Mayor Campbell his due. The fair-grounds looked terrific, decked out with red, white, and green bunting, bleachers adorned in fir and hemlock branches, even the light standards—the town's pride and joy since we had the only lighted ball diamond for fifty miles around—were draped with wreaths and ribbons.

And the activity! There were carnival tents on the south side of the grounds along with a small midway of merry-go-round, Ferris wheel, Tilt-a-Whirl, and whirling teacups. Two long cor-ridors of booths displayed commercial wares that ran heavily to Christmas and winter motifs. A nativity scene had been set up on a flatbed truck parked under a canvas awning, waiting to be unveiled and rolled out for the aerial arrival of the para-chuting Wise Men.

Refreshment booths. Shaved ice stands. Corn dog stands. Hamburger stands. Popcorn stands. A cotton candy machine. And to the delight of Mariposa old-timers, Farmer Hodgins was tending beverage bowls in a stall set a little apart from the others.

Farmer Hodgins—Farmer was his first name, not his profession—was a legendary local bootlegger and former beverage mainstay in the days when the town was dry. Even now, with a liquor outlet and a beer outlet—but still no wine or liquor sold in restaurants—old-timers found themselves complaining that no store-bought potable could compare with Farmer's fabled home distillations. He hadn't been seen around town for some time. His appearance here, behind a huge bowl of fresh strawberry kiddie punch and a sign that said "Try Our Old-Fashioned Punch—Inquire Proprietor" augured pleasantries for a growing mob of thirsty cane-wielding seniors.

There was an outdoor wrestling ring for the midgets, too. (This was a time when the word "midget" was still a come-on to locals, before it became a pejorative word for diminutive people.) The little wrestlers were decked out in jaunty elf costumes and the ring looked like Santa's workshop, but as the wrestlers were a regular summer tourist attraction, it was an attraction too mundane for most.

Still, everything ran like a finely lathed top. The softball tournament plugged along, the men settled comfortably in the bleachers, the kiddies happily rode the rides, the women eyed the goods along the rows of retail stalls, and Mayor Campbell—dressed unaccountably as Long John Silver, complete with eye patch, peg leg, crutch, and stuffed parrot—smiled indulgently as he moved among his people. Over all shone as jaunty and beaming a sun as has ever shone on a town celebrating Christmas in July.

In the weeks that followed, local autopsies performed at various Mariposa morning coffee groups established that the day officially began to roll to hell in a handbasket at 2:02 PM daylight saving time and pinpointed the epicentre of the upheaval as a small wooden table behind the home team bench at the ball diamond.

At the table sat Bert Jones, his Town Crier microphone plugged into the fairground public address system. It was here he announced players, innings, scores, and when special events were beginning where around the grounds.

Nobody paid too much attention to his player introductions, although they did, inning after inning and game after game, begin to take on a seasonal drift, a Christmas theme if you will, developed in a direct mathematical correlation to how much Bert was drinking.

It was assumed, and later ascertained, that Bert began early on the Yuletide eggnog, a beverage provided by the Mariposa chapter of the International Order of the Daughters of the Empire, or IODE, a fine brood of women who remained blissfully unaware that succeeding teams had been spiking the eggnog with rum. The giant punchbowl was originally nestled in crushed ice, but the ice had long since melted and, as unappetizing curds began to surface in the much-meddled-with concoction, players increasingly turned away in favour of nipping directly from their private holiday stock. Bert Jones, too, had turned away from the thickening egg concoction and embraced Farmer Hodgins' return to community life through loyal and large samplings of Farmer's local lightning.

It being a happy day, and Bert happy to be stationary while speaking into a microphone, he was pleased to honour the Christmas season with oratorical stylings he felt sure would be welcomed by his all-ages audience.

"Now batting for Mariposa Township Volunteer Firemen, Santa's little helper, Barney Swanson. On deck, Donder. Blitzen's in the hole." That sort of thing. Nobody seemed to mind, not in a game umpired by a heavyset sweating Santa.

It was when the second baseman of Ivor's Plumbing Supplies advanced to the plate that Bert made his mistake.

"Now batting for Ivor's Plumbing Supplies, Tommy Shenton, a right jolly old elf."

Tough guy Tommy Shenton stopped in his tracks. Tommy was sensitive about elves as a result of a comment once made by his former wife. It was a comment Tommy never understood but worried was a slur upon his manhood. So hearing the word over the public address system caused him to turn, walk over to the announcer, slam his bat on the table, and air his displeasure.

Bert was at first puzzled at the interruption, then angry and displeased with Tommy's reaction to an innocuous seasonal remark. Bert became agitated himself. So agitated he forgot to take his finger off the transmit button. The entire fairground was thus privy to the right jolly old elf's colourful and highly personal intention to rearrange Bert's anatomy in interesting ways.

The audience was also able—thanks to Bert's rock steady finger on the button—to share in most of Bert's equally colourful reply, at least until he took his hand off the button to protect his head from the blows that began to rain down from both the second baseman's mitt hand and throwing hand.

The resulting fight brought Santa hustling over from behind home plate. With no preliminary mediation, Santa waded into the fray and heaved the two combatants in opposite directions.

Unfortunately, Santa heaved Bert into a covey of Allied Roofing infielders who had been salving their first-game loss with heavy applications of healing lubricants. The ball players let fly against Bert, both for his sudden weight and for his earlier remarks concerning Allied Roofing being a lot of red-nosed dears.

A number of locals sprang to the Town Crier's defence, and pretty soon there was a heaving mass of ball players, Farmer's seniors with their canes, cottagers in their Bermuda shorts and suntan oil, an elf or two, assorted Santas and their helpers, and—trying to break it up and restore order to the day—the mayor, Long John Silver himself.

It took some time to end the melee, with warring parties sent to various parts of the field to reflect upon their sins. Bert Jones was ejected for conduct unbecoming a public address announcer. They tried to restart the ball game, but players continued to return to the scene to argue various points of sporting fair play. The mayor was about to make an announcement over the public address system on the need for universal brotherhood at this festive time of season when he became aware the microphone was missing. Bert had taken his microphone with him when he left.

This fact became public knowledge when Bert's amplified voice was suddenly heard from outside the fairgrounds.

"You're all a fucking bunch of fucking low-life bastards," Bert Jones announced from the driver's seat in the Town Crier.

It was only his opening salvo.

As the Nash and its loud speaker toured slowly along the bordering street, Bert gave voice to characterizations of assorted ballplayers and their spouses—as well as certain municipal officials—and described their personality traits and sexual proclivities as he conceived them to be.

I don't know if you've ever been in a large room that's suddenly fallen silent with everyone listening in embarrassment to a haranguing voice, but I ask you to imagine an entire outdoor fairground which—save for the cheerful low background sound of the merry-go-round calliope—is rendered mute by a single electrified voice from a loudspeaker atop a moving 1957 white-and-sunburst-yellow Nash Metropolitan. It really was rather dramatic.

At least the adults seemed to think so. They had turned into stone statues.

Us kids, however, were absorbing everything Bert said like blotters. We were learning new words and phrases and discovering how old ones could be used in novel ways. Who knew a single procreative verb could have so many adjectives, adverbs, and prefixes? It was a real boost for youth vocabulary and education.

The fairground stillness seemed to stretch out as the little car and its inebriated driver patrolled the perimeter and continued to offer up ribald remarks about this person's unhappy marriage or that person's mysterious trips to a clinic in the city. It wasn't until the Town Crier turned his attention to the mayor, and the word "kickback" was first heard, that the silence was broken.

Mayor Campbell, pirate coat hanging from one arm and turning purple in an effort to untie his bound leg, screamed at the police chief to apprehend the offending driver.

"Shoot out his tires if you need to!"

A police cruiser, its lights flashing and siren wailing, tore out of the grounds and quickly came up behind the Nash.

The Nash didn't stop.

"You can't catch me, fuzzball!" Bert announced through his loudspeaker.

As police chases go, it was a slow one. The Nash simply putted along, blocking forward progress of the police car until the police driver, tiring of Bert's antics and running insults, gunned it to pull alongside and angle the Nash into someone's front yard.

The Nash churned through a flower garden and came to rest against the steps of a front porch.

Nobody saw what happened next because public attention dramatically diverted to the sky where all religious hell was breaking loose.

Having no radio contact with the fairground and running on the clock, the airplane carrying the three wise men had discharged its cargo right on time and the parachutists were duly plummeting earthward.

All three chutes popped and made a very pretty sight, what with the coloured smoke flares attached to jumping boots and the balletic thrashings of the pilgrims as they attempted to remove their biblical clothing from around their heads and necks where it had become rucked and tangled during their descent.

Finally able to see, and wisely noting that the planned landing spot contained no visible nativity scene but rather a roiling mob of people, the chutists diverted to less populated areas about the grounds.

The jumper who bore frankincense actually managed to land on the nativity scene, although the latter was still cloaked and under wraps, so that when he crashed into it, the canvas awning tore away to reveal a different tableau than the one originally intended by organizers.

Yes, there was the Virgin Mary, and there was the young Joseph, but they appeared to be rewriting their historical roles in favour of a more active and hands-on interpretation of the text. Joseph was, in fact, grasping the Virgin Mary, as played by the magistrate's daughter, and was in the process of removing her outer raiment. This visual revelation promoted a certain outpouring of comment from onlookers, most of it of a highly secular and snickering nature.

The bearer of gold, trailing yellow smoke, scored a direct hit on Farmer Hodgins' stall, causing a great clatter as punchbowls were upset and two cases of concealed bottles smashed. A wail of anguish arose and rent the air as patrons reacted to the sight of all that precious beverage soaking into the parched earth.

Myrrh, meanwhile, floated gently to earth in the middle of the reindeer paddock.

The reindeer—jumpy after a long overnight truck ride and nettled at having jockeys on their backs for more than half an hour while waiting for the ball diamond brawl to dissipate—took the arrival of the wise man as a signal for activity. They bolted from the corral in an antlered pack, carrying or dragging their riders here and there about the fairgrounds. Reindeer apparently like to run—and run together as a pack—for they ran together for a long, long time.

Yet it was scarcely a minute later, with no time for fairgoers to fully absorb recent events, that rocketeer Rocky Barnes—situated offsite and also working on a clockwork schedule—joined the festivities.

I don't know if you remember the brief popularity of rocket-packed stunt flyers, but they operated within certain scientific strictures. One was that the strapped-on-the-back rocket pack was designed for short up-and-down vertical hops of a precise height and measured distance equal to the amount of fuel available. Another was that the flier should remain upright and in control of the rocket at all times.

When Barnes blasted off from a parking lot two blocks away, it was with the intention of landing on his feet at a fixed spot at a fixed time. Finding his landing site occupied by a milling crowd that included multiple Santas, bleeding ballplayers, midget wrestlers, inebriated cottagers, and cane-wielding seniors, to say nothing of a herd of marauding reindeer, Rocky quickly calculated that he lacked sufficient fuel to soar skyward and to safety, so he did what any panicked and out-of-options rocketeer would do. He veered sideways.

Right into the big tent, where Big Al Parker was urging a troop of young baton twirlers to finish their act before his cameras ran out of film. The sudden roaring appearance of a horizontal rocketeer crashing into the *Tiny Tot Talent Time* set, combined with the upset of Big Al's favourite hairpiece becoming untethered in the jet wash and trampled upon, sent 'the biggest kid of all' diving for cover under a bench of kindergarteners where he was heard to exclaim that ratings be damned, if he didn't see another effing ankle biter again it would still be too effing soon.

Turns out the cameras had plenty of film. It was terrific television.

I sort of lost track of specific events after that, what with the appearance of the fire truck and ambulance and the reindeer still bucking about. The only thing I remember clearly is the sight of the mayor on the ground, where he had lain since being run down by a careering reindeer—the creature could be seen lapping contentedly from a large punch bowl of what appeared to be egg salad—looking up at my father and saying, "Well, Jimbo, that ought to make the papers."

It did.

The town was given a two-photo front page layout in the *Toronto Telegram* under the headline "Christmas Chaos Result of Rampaging Reindeer," and front page pictures in the *Toronto Star*—"Toronto resident injured in Yuletide Stampede—*Star* man speaks with survivors"—and even the staid old *Globe & Mail* made mention of Mariposa under the calmer headline, "Retail Slump Blamed on Dominion Day Fracas."

Fallout from Christmas in July continued for years.

No local business was inclined to unduly commercialize Christmas. Even when a mall opened years later, its out-of-town owners were persuaded from staging extravagant Yuletide promotions for fear of offending local sentiment, particularly the sentiment of the town magistrate, who was said to be sensitive on the subject.

After a brief stint as replacement host of *Tiny Tot Talent Time*, Bert Jones hung up his microphone and parked the 1957 white-and-sunburst-yellow Nash Metropolitan for good. You could still find him, though, manning the admission gate at the community centre and tearing tickets.

They tell me his last day at the rink was very moving.

The public address announcer paid tribute to Bert's long career, calling him a pioneer in public announcing. On behalf of the community, the announcer thanked him too for his many years of ticket-taking community service.

Sadly, Bert didn't hear the announcer.

He couldn't.

He'd been rendered deaf by all those years in the Nash under its massive loudspeaker.

So it was that on his last day, not only could he not hear the town paying tribute to him, he also couldn't hear the public announcer welcome players and fans to the rink for the Mariposa Midget Hockey Yuletide Tournament, proudly sponsored by Campbell Hardware and its proprietor, Miss Betty Jean Campbell.

Old Will and
Mrs. Whitby

THE HOUSES TO which I'd delivered newspapers on the route toward Bayside are gone.

The brown bungalow of Mrs. Weatherwax, who parked the town's only Chrysler Imperial in her driveway, now replaced by an Arts and Crafts style house.

The Dyson house, a vaguely barn-like structure, torn down in favour of a two-story stucco thing.

The Sheridan's white bungalow, with its green-and-cream shutters, a memory.

At least Mrs. Whitby's house is still here, but it is so altered as to be unrecognizable. Its distinctive brown shingles have been replaced by shiny siding, an extra storey has been added so its roofline is high and unfamiliar, and its entrance path of large flat stones in a left-right-left pattern through high hedges has been replaced by asphalt.

This one hurt. Not for any architectural uniqueness but because it was home to a signature small town story which, when it unfolded, changed how I saw the world. Maybe changed how some in the town saw the world, too.

This had been the house of Mrs. Whitby, but it was also the first Mariposa home of William St. Williams—Old Will—and he was a game changer. Old Will wasn't the first dark-skinned man the town had seen, but he was the first I'd ever seen. In those days, a black man in a northern Ontario town was bound to stick out some.

Small towns can initially be terrible places for an outsider or an immigrant. Not because we were intolerant of race, skin, or religion. On the contrary. Anybody could come and be anything they wanted to be in our town, so long as it was legal and so long as we all agreed what it was. Or in the case of Farmer Hodgins, the town bootlegger, a fellow could pursue a less-than-legal path so long as it suited the social fabric. Once you knew a person, the person was accepted.

Old Will wasn't shunned. People served him in their stores and restaurants and smiled at him on the street and said hello in the politest of voices. It's just that when he first arrived the smiles were a little too tight, a little too polite. This reaction—to skin colour, to race, to religion—was because people were so worried about setting a hoof wrong that they simply froze up and ceased to be their nosy selves. It's why nobody knew much about Old Will beyond the facts that he was obviously old, obviously black, and obviously out of place. Certainly, they didn't know what brought him to Mariposa in the first place—or more important, why he chose to stay.

I did, though.

I was there when it happened.

However, I should first say a few words about Mrs. Whitby and her house.

Mrs. Dorothy Whitby was the whitest person in Mariposa. Her hair might have had a blue sheen but her skin was white parchment with only the slightest trace of powder. She had an aristocratic face and a long straight nose and a piercing eye that could slam a kid's mouth shut at a dozen paces.

She was originally one half of the famous married act of Mr. and Mrs. John Whitby, owners of the local furniture store. John was the businessman, a balding and slightly fussy little fellow who was always sneezing and cleaning his spectacles with his shirtsleeve. Dorothy supplied the exquisite taste. She was tall and regal and seemed to sail along a sidewalk on casters. She raised two children by the book, saw them settled in the nicer part of Toronto, and then—after John keeled over dead in the store—settled into her mission in life, the pursuit of fine music.

Mrs. Whitby was a subscribing patron of the Toronto symphony, choral society, opera society, baroque society, and any other Toronto society that offered the prospect of classical music performed live and well in a pleasant setting. Every year she travelled on a grand tour to New York, London, and Berlin to indulge her tastes.

There were rumours that in her younger days she'd had a torrid affair with Herbert von Karajan, the Austrian conductor of the Berlin Philharmonic, but that was probably just town talk and nothing to do with the dozen or so Deutsche Grammophon records she received each month by parcel post or the letters she would occasionally post to a Maestro von Karajan.

Her house, with its decent reading chairs and Blaupunkt stereo, was a rambling post-and-beam affair set amid pleasant lawns and professionally tended gardens. The property was notable to the neighbourhood kids because it had a fabulous two-storey boathouse built into a steep lakeside bank. In the boathouse proper, which was always left open, were an unused canoe, a rowboat riddled with dry rot, and the largest colony of daddy-long-leg spiders in town. Above, set flush into the lawn on its house side, was a wonderful little one-bedroom apartment, with a wall of painted wooden frame windows overlooking the lake. Attached to the boathouse was an addition of a single large room.

In life, John Whitby's passions had been billiards, Benny Goodman, and Bix Beiderbecke, and Mrs. Whitby wasn't having any of them in the house. So John had a contractor build a large extension onto the boathouse. In it he installed a fireplace, the biggest billiards table that Brunswick made, and a very nice McIntosh sound system. While Dorothy occupied herself with her books and her high-brow music on one side of the lawn, John indulged his passions on the other side.

As far as us kids were concerned, Mrs. Whitby was just the tall old lady up the street who, if you spotted her outside the battlements of her hedges, caused you to slow to a walk, keep your voice down, and move along in an orderly fashion until it was safe to resume being the low-browed delinquent she assumed you to be.

Let us leave Mrs. Whitby there for now, up the street listening to her records and reading her books, and proceed to a summer's day when my father brought home an unexpected guest for lunch.

An unexpected lunch guest was not an unusual event at our house. My father—because of his profession and because of his nature—was forever arriving home with an unexpected lunch guest. He was editor and publisher of the local paper, so people with something to sell in Mariposa made my father one of their first stops. Politicians, businessmen, con artists, if any of them arrived at the newspaper before lunch and if my father was interested to hear what they had to say, well, he was the type of person who'd invite them to lunch. Which, if it happened to be summer, meant inviting them to our house, because my dad always came home for lunch—the office was just five minutes away—for a quick swim and his inevitable tray of peanut butter sandwich, skim milk, and stewed rhubarb on the lakefront porch where he'd read a magazine—*Yachting, Illustrated London News, Sports Illustrated*, or MAD—with the windows open and the breeze coming in off the lake. It was this lunchtime ritual that caused him to turn down job offers from the Toronto papers. He was mildly interested in the jobs but in the end, you really can't beat coming home for a quick dip and lunch on the porch when the breeze is coming in off the lake.

I don't think it ever occurred to my father that my mother might have to scramble to come up with something for a guest to eat on these occasions, something other than peanut butter, skim milk, and stewed rhubarb. Ours was not a house with a well-stocked larder or fridge. We never went hungry, but my mother had very few things on hand that weren't earmarked for breakfast or dinner. Maybe a little baloney, or a couple of cheese slices, but nothing like the sort of fare you'd be tempted to offer Premier John Robarts or Lord Thomson of Fleet or the Minister of National Defence, all of whom my father brought home unannounced for lunch.

What my mother would always do whenever she heard two car doors at lunchtime was come to the door, smile a genuine smile, shake a hand, and repair to the kitchen to make a baloney or a cheese slice sandwich and then cut off the crusts and slice the sandwich into little triangles. She'd sprinkle a few cherry tomatoes on the plate and bring it out to the porch and hope it did the job.

It seemed to. It seemed to do just fine. And why wouldn't it? The food might not be memorable but the breeze coming in off the lake usually made the guest feel he was having a better lunch than could be found in any stuffy city restaurant.

Me, I wasn't always sure whether the guest was a politician or a con artist, but my father said this was a common mistake in our town and not to worry about it. "The secret is to let them tell their story," he said. "You'll know who's who and what's what if you let them have their say."

Sometimes a lunch guest was a pure wild card. Like the day my dad brought home Percy Leggett.

Percy was a tramp. The real thing, complete with a bag on the end of a walking stick carried on his shoulder. Percy had been hitchhiking on the highway when my father saw him and, attracted by the stick and bag, stopped and picked him up and brought him home for a swim and lunch on the porch.

Percy washed himself and his clothes in the lake and my mother hung the apparel on the clothesline in the sun and in the snapping breeze off the lake and then proceeded to clean his shoes. The image of my mother scraping and polishing a tramp's shoes couldn't have shocked me more than if she'd knelt and anointed Percy's feet with oil and dried them with her hair. It was a side of her I'd never seen. She brought him little triangle cheese sandwiches—the same ones she'd brought to the premier. He helped himself to two helpings of stewed rhubarb while he and my father had a good old talk on the porch while I was out on the lawn batting acorns with Percy's seasoned walking stick.

Three days later, my father wrote the following in the *Mariposa Daily Packet & Times*:

> Percy Leggett, the bearded hermit and tramp who professed to have resigned from the human race, is dead, victim of a highway accident on a darkened road... [T]his weary, tattered but curiously valiant figure, whose clothes and manners and behaviour were such an embarrassment to us all, was an embodiment of our conscience, and a reproach to the compromises we have all made to achieve the comfort of conformity in a conformist society. All of us who ever dreamed of "getting out of the old rat race"; who have secretly envied the waifs and strays sleeping in the sun whom we pass on the way to work; who have forced ourselves into a clean collar and the dreary formality of a banquet meeting when we would rather have been out on the lake, fishing the evening rise; all we weaklings who have surrendered and made ourselves conform to the wearisome pattern of a shallow society, have envied the Percy Leggetts of this world.

Yes sir, a boy could pick up some life lessons when unexpected guests showed up for lunch. I know I did, especially the day my father showed up and announced that Mr. William St. Williams would be taking lunch on the porch.

As I understand it, my father had been on his way home, driving along Bay Street, when he saw this old black man with a small suitcase walking along the road. My dad stopped, asked the man if he needed directions or a ride, and when he heard the man's reply, brought him home for lunch.

My father and Mr. St. Williams seemed to be having a fine philosophical discussion over sandwiches and rhubarb—I caught the names of Burke and Vauban and Clausewitz—and after, I went in with my mother ostensibly to remove dishes but really to sit and listen. My mother asked Mr. St. Williams where he was from, and I had to lean in to catch his raspy baritone reply.

He came from the Deep South, he said. He had first worked in Mississippi as a piano player but later moved in the 1920s to Harlem, and had travelled everywhere in the US.

He was a widower, he said, his only daughter dying young. He retired from piano playing because of his hands. He held them up for us to see. They looked like two gnarled woodcarvings. When he stopped playing piano professionally, he took a notion to find a little town where he could live peacefully and read and watch the seasons change over a little lake.

"I walked from town to town, and I headed north," he said. "I'm very partial to your little lake here. Just the right size. So's the town."

"You walked?" I blurted. "From New York?"

Seeing my incredulous face, he smiled. "I like walking, young man. You get the feel of places and the people in them in a way you can't when you whiz by in cars or trains or planes. I've done enough riding in my piano-playing days to last a lifetime. But I was just asking your dad here if there might be a little house for sale or rent along this street, a place where I might settle in and send for my things."

My father looked at my mother and said, "I was thinking about Mrs. Whitby's boathouse."

My mother said she wasn't sure if Mrs. Whitby was looking for a lodger.

"I think Will and I should go see her," my father said. "You never know."

Personally, I found the notion of Mrs. Whitby allowing anyone to live in her compound insane, but I kept my mouth shut.

Father telephoned Mrs. Whitby to see if she could meet, and he and Old Will walked up the drive and turned up the street toward the Whitby house.

I later learned from my mother what happened.

Father and Old Will were just coming up the path of large flat stones in the left-right-left pattern that led through the high hedges to the Whitby house when Mrs. Whitby met them. She was using a cane and she stumbled. Old Will shot out an arm, which she grabbed to steady herself.

"Are you all right, Ma'am?" Old Will said.

"Perfectly fine, thank you," Mrs. Whitby said.

When telling the story, my mother always pauses at this point. "Your father thinks this was an important moment. He thinks that in that moment, some sort of kindness passed between the two of them. Certainly there was something. There's no other explanation for what happened next."

What happened next was my father introduced William St. Williams, explained his quest for a little house or cabin on the lake and how my father had thought immediately of the Whitby boathouse, and had Mrs. Whitby ever given any thought to having a tenant in it?

"No," she said. A beat. "However, I suppose if Mr. St. Williams would like to see the place for himself, there'd be no harm in that."

Old Will went to the boathouse, inspected the apartment and the billiards room, came back to where my father and Mrs. Whitby stood, and delivered a line that my father would quote for years after: "Ma'am, you've got yourself a bird's nest on the ground there. I'd be honoured to take it if you're offering."

Surprising everyone, and likely herself, Mrs. Whitby said Mr. St. Williams was welcome to take up residence in the boathouse.

Which he did. William St. Williams—Old Will to everyone except Mrs. Whitby, who continued to call him Mr. St. Williams—took up residence on Bay Street in Mariposa.

There was some small talk by some small portion of the community—no more than 90 percent of the townsfolk, surely—about how odd it seemed that Mrs. Whitby would have Old Will on the property, and not for any reason of race or skin colour, you understand, but simply because it was assumed Mrs. Whitby didn't like anyone, living or dead.

Beyond that, there wasn't much to report from the Whitby compound, except that Old Will sent for his things. Which turned out to be—courtesy the surveillance of the owner of the cartage company—several dozen large boxes, books to judge by the weight of them, and a crate that took four men to move through the double doors of the old billiards room and turned out to be a piano.

And he wasn't poor. This was courtesy of the bank manager who mentioned it in confidence to a few banking colleagues over coffee, whereupon it proceeded to percolate its way through the town. Old Will was not loaded to the gills, but he enjoyed a bank balance that all but a few in town would have been proud to possess.

And with that, Old Will became one of us.

Known, yes. Accepted, yes. But really, not well understood. It would be a few months before my family came to some deeper understanding of Old Will.

It was two weeks before Christmas when I heard his overshoes going *ker-flup ker-flup ker-flup* down our driveway. He knocked on the door and asked my mother if the family might be interested in dropping by his little boathouse Christmas Eve for some piano music, William St. Williams-style.

You bet we would.

We knocked on the boathouse door on Christmas Eve, and there was Old Will, dressed in a tuxedo. The room was sparsely furnished, the lakefront windows frosted, but it was warm and cozy. He took our coats and hung them on a hook on the wall. He said Mrs. Whitby might or might not be along and we stood around awkwardly while he brought a hot chocolate for me, sherry for my mother, single malt for my father, and a soda water for himself. He proposed a toast—"To helping hands! To higher destinations!"—and we toasted the evening. There was a knock at the door and there stood Mrs. Whitby, wearing a dark wrap like a monk's robe. Old Will asked if he might take her coat, and she gave it over, revealing herself to be dressed for the opera—gown, jewelled necklace, diamond earrings, everything.

"Why, Mrs. Whitby," Old Will said. "You honour us."

"Thank you," Mrs. Whitby said, accepting a sherry.

Old Will said that as we were all here, we might as well go in.

The billiards room had been converted into what looked like a gentleman's club. There was oak panelling, floor-to-ceiling bookcases, comfortable armchairs, and a fireplace with apple wood sparking and snapping happily behind an antique fire screen. The centrepiece of the room was a grand piano that gleamed in some places and glowed in others, as if some of its shine had rubbed off on the people who'd leaned against it. On the piano were a candle and two brown-and-white photographs. One was of a handsome young black man in a tuxedo leaning leisurely against a grand piano. The other was of a beautiful young black woman holding a baby in her arms.

My father was impressed by the room. My mother was astonished. I was delighted. Difficult to say what Mrs. Whitby was thinking.

"I tend to do my daily living—and all my summer living—in the other room," Old Will said, reading our thoughts. "This is where I hibernate in winter. Reading and playing. Here is where I . . ." He searched for the right words. "I guess you might say that here is where my heart lives."

He ushered us to the armchairs, saw to our drinks, and seated himself carefully on the piano bench.

He clasped his hands before his chest, as if in prayer. He stared at the picture of the young woman and child. The only sound was the soft hissing of logs in the fireplace.

Then he slowly brought his hands down, closed his eyes, and touched the keys.

The room filled with majesty.

He began with a sonata, slow and pure, the notes hanging like physical objects, visible and shimmering.

He moved into stride piano, light as summer rain, and then pushed into boogie-woogie and barrelhouse. He ran through what I would later learn was a selection of songs by Duke Ellington, Scott Joplin, and Fats Waller.

I had never heard—have never heard to this day—a performance to match it. He sat erect as he played. There was no trace of his characteristic old man's slouch. His hands seemed to be the hands of a younger man. He would sometimes call out a name or phrase—"Duke!" or "Yes, yes, yes!" or "Jump it!"— to indicate either authorship or an exhortation to an unseen audience. Always, his eyes stared straight ahead at something I couldn't see, something that wasn't in the room.

I have a good memory, but I couldn't tell you if Old Will's recital was twenty minutes or two hours. All I know was that it was terrific. My parents thought so, too. And Mrs. Whitby, although she seemed as unmoved and chilly as always, I can tell you her eyes were wide open. Whatever she was feeling, she was feeling it plenty.

Eventually Old Will took a break and we bombarded him with questions. After freshening our drinks, he regaled us with stories of his days playing piano, of cutting contests with the likes of a young Duke Ellington at rent parties, of life on the black piano circuit of the 1920s and 1930s, of living in the back room of Sidney Bechet's Harlem cleaning business, how he believed he was a pretty good piano player but James P. Johnson, Fats Waller, and Willie "The Lion" Smith were better, and how and why a man named Art Tatum was the best of them all.

Finally, my mother asked about the photograph of the young woman and child.

"She was my wife," he said. "The little one was my daughter. They were killed Christmas Eve many years ago."

"How?" my mother asked.

"In a car accident," he said. "I was driving."

He asked us if we would like to sing a carol, it being Christmas Eve. My father suggested "Away in a Manger." Old Will turned back to the keys and we sang it. Mrs. Whitby did not join in, but Old Will did, in a voice that sounded nothing like his speaking voice. It sounded good.

He played what seemed to be a sort of calypso tune called "Mary Had a Boy Child." I had never heard it before and was surprised my mother not only knew all the words but could sing it in a boisterous, rollicking voice.

More astounding was that Mrs. Whitby evidently knew the tune, too, and joined in with a small voice that sounded like it was coming from an attic.

My father finally said that it was late and that we should be going, and my mother told Old Will and Mrs. Whitby not to get up, that we'd see ourselves out. My father and I shook old Will's hand, my mother kissed him on the cheek. My mother never kissed anyone, and Old Will seemed to know it.

"Piano players," he said. "We get all the kisses."

Outside, my father and mother and I paused to breathe in the crisp winter air and savour the bright moonlight on the white expanse of the frozen lake.

We were about to walk toward the high hedges and the road when we heard the piano.

It was "Adeste Fideles." We listened.

From out of the boathouse came the sound of singing. It was Old Will, but this was not the voice we'd heard earlier. This was a booming voice, full of fire. This was the voice of a man in his prime, and it was joined by the voice of Mrs. Whitby, itself full of gusto. Both seemed to be singing from another time, another place.

My father put his arm around my mother, the other on my shoulder. We stood for a moment as outsiders and listened as the two inside sent the carol out over the snows and up into the moon-bright heavens.

Then we went home.

The Kids
Are All Right

MOVING ALONG THE lake side of the street, there's
the Farrell house—Mrs. Farrell is still alive at 105
and living at home. It looks exactly the same as it did
years earlier, a rambling green shingle house that, then as now,
hides behind a twenty-foot-high untrimmed hedge.

Next is J.W. Park's old place, still recognizable though the
Park family is long gone. Behind the two-storey brick house,
unseen on the high-bank shore, is the concrete wet-slip boathouse that J.W. built to shelter his massive Sheppard speedboat.
This gleaming mahogany aquatic wonder towed as many as
12 water skiers at a time up and down the waterfront—what
my father called "J.W.'s Flying Circus"—with his son Robert
and all his friends calling to one another at the end of their ski
ropes, yelling and laughing over the sound of skis slapping on
the water on a Mariposa weekend.

Time was when the triple-wide Park driveway out front
boasted a half-dozen new Pontiacs and Buicks and Oldsmo-
biles parked to create what J.W. called "my second showroom."
Faded but still visible is the little patch of asphalt that J.W. had
put in for son Robert's red Firebird convertible, the third car off

the line in its inaugural GM production run and, along with his sixteen-year-old son, the apple of J.W.'s eye.

I remember the day Robert was killed by a drunk driver and how J.W. came home in the late afternoon to be met on the front steps by his wife and how they sat down right there on the concrete stairs, their arms around one another and their heads bowed together, and how they stayed there for a long, long time, with the neighbourhood afraid to approach with flowers and food and condolences.

We never again heard the joyous sound of J.W.'s Flying Circus along the shoreline. Skis and lifebelts and ropes were stowed in the boathouse. J.W.'s magnificent craft would only occasionally appear in the evening, when J.W. would take the boat out on the lake, turn off the engine and drift and contemplate the setting sun.

The next house was old Doc Hipwell's summer place and it, too, seemed much the same, or at least what you could see of it behind a massive wooden fence. The house itself—a lovely pile of stone and wood and turn-of-the-century wavy glass— had been purchased after Doc's death by a drug dealer and turned into a walled compound so obvious and clichéd that it seemed as if the owner wanted to advertise his status as a narcotics kingpin.

The next house after that—well, I knew it as well as I'd ever known a house other than my own. It belonged to Stu and Shirley Donald, parents of Paul Donald, my childhood best friend.

A childhood best friend is a one-and-done proposition. You're of the same sex. You're of the same age. You are friends because of proximity, not because of nature. You don't plan it, you don't question it, you just go out and do everything together. You don't think about it being the most important relationship outside your family, the one that will determine whether you are a leader or a follower, the one that will slowly swing your moral compass one way or another and provide you with early life lessons.

The childhood best friend thing is, by definition, fleeting. At some point, probably in elementary school and certainly by high school, you begin to move apart. There are other people you want to hang out with. If you're a typical boy, the hormones arrive and there will be girls to consider.

The friendship doesn't end in anger or dispute—it just drifts away, as it must when experiences are no longer shared. It's only years later when you come across it in the bottom drawer and pull it out and examine it in the light that you realize how important it once was, how it took up the hours and days and weeks and months and years of your early life, and how you never once gave it a thought.

As I stand in front of the familiar yellow brick bungalow two doors up from my house, I'm not even looking at the Donald house. I'm looking at my childhood, looking back to my earliest memories and the world I inhabited with my best friend, Paul Donald.

Paul's parents built the house and moved in when I was four, but I have no recollection of meeting Paul for the first time, only that he and I were always doing something together.

Running.

Jumping.

Falling down.

The above happened daily, practically hourly, and the attendant cuts, scrapes, and bruises required motherly application of Dettol antiseptic and box after box of Band-Aids. I once fell face-first off the stair rail of Paul's boathouse to the stones and gravel below, forcing my mother to treat my facial cuts with the only Band-Aids she had on hand, which were brightly coloured and adorned with battleships. My father said my face resembled a re-enactment of the Battle of Jutland.

Tag.

Hide and seek.

Acorn fights.

Sticks.

This was a game Paul and I invented and played every evening for an entire summer on the street in front of our houses. The game went like this: collect piles of twigs and small sticks from under the maples and elms and oaks along the street and, when the coast was clear, toss a whole bunch of them on the street and stand around until you hear a car coming. At that point you hurl yourself into the hedge, or dive behind a pile of leaves, or flatten yourself into a shallow depression in the empty field across the road and wait for the sound of the car's tires to go crackling and crunching over the sticks, and after the car has passed, you pop up and laugh hysterically together and go chum the road again. In hindsight, this might seem a colossally senseless and stupid game, but at that time in our lives it was the absolute height of adventure, sport, and sophisticated wit. There really wasn't a better way to spend an hour or two after dinner and before bedtime on a summer's evening than playing sticks with your best friend. It sent you to bed in a good mood and promoted such a restful sleep that it's a wonder doctors don't prescribe it to insomniacs.

Cycling.

It began with tricycles—the real metal ones, not the reclined-seat plastic sort that would later come to dominate a kid's early years.

The tricycle you rode was the one possession that defined you in the neighbourhood, and I got lucky because my father brought home a big used one, the tall kind you could stand up on the rear-wheel steps of and lean over on the handlebars and steer down the hill at wild speeds. (Remember, tricycles didn't have brakes and while you could pedal forward or backward, you could never pedal as fast as the pedals could revolve on their own going down a hill, so you had to get your feet off the pedals and get your backside off the seat and stand up on the trike's rear-wheel steps to get up a head of serious velocity.) Ours were customized with handlebar ribbons and bulb horns and wooden apple baskets tied on with string to carry whatever a five-year-old might find on his rounds of the neighbourhood.

When you finally learned to ride a two-wheeler—your dad running alongside in support until you physically and figuratively left him behind—it opened up the town. In a stroke, you could wheel out of the familiar confines of your street and neighbourhood and travel to strange new worlds and explore everything everywhere and still manage to be home for supper.

Say what you like about the automobile opening up horizons, the bicycle opened them first.

Me with my one-speed CCM and Paul with his three-speed Raleigh, there was nowhere in town we didn't go. Our bikes could be found on their kickstands next to woods and ponds and streams or downtown in front of the small-town department stores—Metropolitan, Woolworth's, Chainway. And Leatherdale Marine where we'd ogle the hot outboard motors, and the United Cigar Store and Newsstand where the best comics were, and the Army Surplus store where they had machetes and flare guns and two- and four-inch cannon firecrackers on display, and above all, in front of the Mariposa Hobby and Record store with its racks of LPs and 45s and its shelves of games and train sets and slot car sets.

Slot cars.

Long before the little Hot Wheels took over the market, there was a vogue for slot cars, the ⅟₃₂ scale replicas with high-winding electric engines and a steering peg flanked by two conducting leads that fitted into a routed slot on a race track. With a hand controller that you mashed down with your thumb, these little rockets wound up and whizzed around various tracks, the best of them being a custom layout in the basement of the Mariposa Hobby and Record store. With my souped-up Strombecker Ferrari and Paul's AMF Ford GT, we torched all comers until we met our match in a couple of older kids who had dropped *two* electric motors each into their cars and fitted their controllers with graduated braking and beat us going away. We carried on for a while at a homemade track in Kathy Farrell's house on Bay Street—her father and older brother were small-scale motor addicts—but to get to their basement involved running a gauntlet of Kathy and her girl-friends and in those pre-hormonal days it seemed more work than the hobby was worth, so we drifted off the tracks.

Mr. Donald put a pool table in the basement when we were eleven and we spent a lot of time down there getting our game in shape, playing to jukebox music and perfecting bank shots and learning to stroke the cue ball with an unlit cigarette dangling from our lips.

But in truth, anything to do with front yards or basements of our houses was always second banana to the attractions of the backyard that fronted the lake. The backyard was king, and nowhere more so than at Paul's place where it was graded level and his parents would play croquet with the neighbours, Mr. Donald being something of a croquet shark. Paul and I learned to play, and it was a game that later stood me in good stead in Ottawa and Vancouver in cutthroat games against ginned-up cabinet ministers and pompous celebrities.

Paul's backyard extended to a high embankment that plunged down to the water and a small sand beach, the only real sand beach on the street between Mariposa Beach Park and Bayside. The sand accumulated here because of the Donalds' wet-slip boathouse that extended out from the shore and trapped the sand on its lee side. There was a sitting area atop the boathouse, reached by the original exterior stairs—the ones I fell from—and later by a skyway Mr. Donald had built so you could walk from the lawn right to the top of the boathouse, which we re-purposed as a kind of elevated jungle gym.

On the far side of the property above the beach was what they called "the shack," a one-room summer cabin, with two old wrought-iron hospital beds and a permanent smell of mice, that Paul and I used for sleepovers, or to clamber up onto its roof where—using a thick rope tied to a birch tree limb—we'd swing down over the beach and drop into about two inches of lake water.

The swing was really only interesting to us when Paul's parents were out of the house and we could dig out a shallow trench in the sand, fill it with gasoline, throw a wooden match into it, then swing off the roof and through the flames and drop into the two inches of water with scarcely a scorch mark.

But it was what was in the boathouse that was the attraction. That's where the Donald speedboat was.

Paul's father ran the local photography business—Donald Studios. He did portraits and weddings and sold film, and everyone for fifty square miles dropped their film off at Donald Studios to have it developed. Every year Mr. Donald took photos of every couple at every high school dance and put a copy of each photo in the front window of the store so that the couples—or more often, their parents—could purchase them. Everyone would stand in front of the window and make comments about this boy's hair or that girl's dress or the colourful getups worn to the annual Sadie Hawkins dance at the Mariposa District Collegiate and Vocational Institute. All of this work forced Mr. Donald to put in long hours on weekdays and weekends alike, so he took his home time seriously.

He was the slowest-moving parent on the block, walking as if under water, harbouring his strength for matters beyond mere transit from here to there. But he had a thing for speed—and for being comfortable when moving with speed—and it manifested itself in his choice of autos—a big Buick roadster, then a Ford Thunderbird—and in his choice of marine conveyance. During my youth, he had a succession of three speedboats. Each was fast, flashy, and all-round terrific.

The earliest was a wooden-hulled inboard, a mahogany gem built by Mariposa's Hunter Boats featuring a Chrysler truck engine with clutch pedal and floor accelerator and weighing roughly seventeen million pounds.

One or two evenings a week during the summer, you'd hear a roar as Mr. Donald fired up the behemoth and reversed it out of the boathouse in a haze of blue exhaust fumes before shifting it into forward and slowly accelerating away toward Mariposa Beach Park. It took him about the length of a 747 take-off to come up to a fast cruise. He'd do a wide turn in the bay by the park and then come speeding back along the shoreline—engine roaring, big displacement spray sheeting away from the stern, wearing a look of supreme contentment on his face—before he disappeared down the other direction trailing a powerful wake that would wash noisily along the shore. He'd make a wide sweep out into the middle of the lake and then head back on a straight line for home. The craft took a long distance to slow and he'd coast the boat straight in, ending with a little flourish as he shifted it into reverse and stopped dead inside the boathouse.

Water skiing.

Our water-skiing careers began by mastering a surfboard behind the Donald inboard.

The surfboard isn't what you think it is. It's a three-and-a-half-foot wide by five-foot long rectangular piece of wood with a slight upturn at the front where a rope is attached that runs to the towboat. Two equal-length ropes are attached on each side of the front of the board and joined with a wooden handle to make a kind of bottom-up trapeze that allowed a kid to stand on the board and steer by pulling on one side or the other of the handle, although steering the board was pretty minimal as the board's trailing corners would dig into the boat's enormous wake and throw you off. Still, we learned how to get up on the board and master the balance required to stay aboard. After that, it was a breeze to graduate to two skis, and then to a single slalom ski.

The skiing was great but the boat's wake was so large that you couldn't really slalom from side to side behind it. Also, the engine exhaust was such that on calm days it was like being towed behind a copper smelter.

Mr. Donald soon allowed Paul to take the boat out by himself—usually with me glued to the shotgun seat—and we had a lot of fun tearing around the lake. The only rule we had to follow was that before you started the engine, you had to lift up and pull back the engine box before turning the key. This was to ensure that any gas fumes that might collect in the enclosed engine box were properly vented and thus unable to ignite in a towering fireball.

Paul and I had the kind of keen scientific minds common to our age and gender. It seemed a waste of energy to go back to the stern to open the box, then move up to the front seat to turn the key, then go back to the stern and lower the box, then return to the steering wheel, so one day we dropped into the front seats and knowingly left the box down when we started the engine. A giant finger of flame and smoke shot out of the stern exhaust. We looked at one another. "Cool!"

Explosive fumes in the engine box might not scare us, but the man who filled the tanks and serviced the engine—Harold Bolland of Bolland's Boats—sure did. We'd take the boat down and tie up at his dock and he'd fill it up from the gas pump at a cost equivalent to a father's weekly earnings. On those occasions when the engine required a look-see, Mr. Bolland would hang over the carburetor with the world's longest cigarette ash dangling from his lip. Paul and I would always retreat to the doors of the shop to avoid the explosion we felt sure would follow, but we'd be too scared to stand there for long because Mr. Bolland had a large poster on the door of what looked like a large white shark with enormous gashes across its belly. Upon closer inspection, it wasn't a shark. It was a human body. The poster was to alert boaters to the dangers of needlessly running their propellers over swimmers, and to pay attention to the universal symbol of divers in the water, a red square with a diagonal white slash.

Paul and I learned the actual worth of that symbol.

We were using somebody's Aquaboy outfit—a stunningly unsafe diving apparatus consisting of a lawnmower engine-type compressor set in a floating orange inner tube that sent air down a couple of 25-foot rubber hoses into two glorified underwater masks, all under the supposed protection of a little flagstick flying the diver-in-the-water pennant. We were about 200 feet off the shore from our houses, investigating some sort of wooden cribbing on the lake bottom, and we hadn't been down for two minutes before boats from all around the lake began arriving to see what this floating orange contraption was. The divers-in-the-water symbol didn't act as a "Caution! Keep-away" warning so much as it functioned as a "Hey-what's-that-in-the-water? Let's-go-see-what-it-is!" boat attractor.

The churning propellers above us, the sheer volume of the engine noise in the water, sent us into a panicky paralysis, unable to surface for fear of being cut to shreds and becoming an updated "We told you so!" poster for Bolland's Boats. It was the one and only time we went swimming or diving under the symbol's protection.

Mr. Donald—tired of the hefty gasoline bills—sold the Hunter and bought a high-sided Grew runabout with an inboard-outboard MerCruiser engine. It was a great boat and Paul and I blossomed as water skiers.

We both became adept slalomers, able to zip back and forth across the wake at a near-professional level, bodies parallel to the water's surface coming out of the turns, and soon moved to trick skiing, where Paul in particular excelled. Trick skis were shorter, stubbier affairs able to go backward, forward, sideways, and vertically for jumps and twisting aerial stunts. We learned to ski barefoot, which—once you developed the hang of dropping a ski and transferring your weight onto the soles of your feet without letting your toes dig into the water—was more impressively showy than the talent required to perform it.

After that, Paul and I pretty much went rogue. We took to wearing capes, confident the sight of us skiing back and forth past Mariposa Beach Park would set teenaged hearts to fluttering and the girls talking among themselves. "They're so cool!" "Who are these dashing young men?" "How can I get to know them?"

In reality, if the teenaged girls actually talked about us, it was with expressions such as "show boaters" or "stick insects" or "maroons!"

It didn't help that we were by now skiing on items other than skis. We'd use paddles, mops, brooms, ladders, anything we could manage to stay upright on without killing ourselves. My mother put an end to this phase of our skiing on the day she looked out the picture window and saw her antique rocking chair whizzing by with me—clad in dad's old top hat and tails—trying to balance on its arms.

The third Donald boat was the capper, a gorgeous mahogany Greavette with MerCruiser inboard-outboard. Smaller than its predecessors—maybe sixteen feet in length—it had a creamy upholstered driver's seat and matching tuck-and-roll side seat that curved around to become the rear seat, and a polished afterdeck that housed the engine.

It was—to use a fine old nautical term—pure sex.

You put the throttle down and the boat damn near stood on its stern before leaping forward to plane out at high speed. With its electronic trim tabs, you could raise the hull up so that it was almost riding on the outboard drive unit alone. And yeah, we skied behind it—it was particularly wonderful for barefooting—but by that point, as we hit the ages of sixteen and seventeen, its highest and best use was as a vehicle of travel to Eight Mile Point, otherwise known as the Isthmus of Exotic City Girls.

Paul was now attending St. Andrew's College, a boarding school in Aurora. (His parents wanted to get his marks up.) I was at Ridley College in St. Catharines. (I'd attended Bishop's College in Quebec for a couple of weeks the summer before to improve my French, and my parents—suspecting that the arrival of recreational drugs in our town meant I would soon become involved with them—asked me if I wanted to go to a boy's private school for my final two years of high school. Having had fun at a boy's school for French immersion—and foolishly thinking the lax rules of a summer school would exist during the regular terms of private school—I said sure. I don't know how they afforded it, but they did.)

As a result, Paul and I—through separate channels at our respective schools—got to know some Toronto girls whose parents had cottages at Eight Mile Point on Lake Ossawippi, the larger adjoining body of water to the south. It came to pass that on several occasions during the summer before our final year of high school, I would sneak out of our little summerhouse and Paul would sneak out of his little cabin. We'd meet up at his boathouse and paddle the Greavette out of its slip and down the lake a distance before firing it up and setting off on a dark-of-the-night high-speed run across our lake, through the Narrows, and down to Eight Mile Point where we'd rendezvous with any of the Toronto girls—Michelle, Joanne, Kim, Cathy—who could get their big city selves out through their small cottage bathroom windows.

Eight Mile Point was where a Toronto Maple Leafs player who operated a Mariposa hockey camp had his cottage. Out walking with the girls at 2 AM, we'd see a fleet of dark blue sedans from a Toronto dealership parked on his lawn, the young Leafs passed out on the grass in a sea of empties.

Paul and I had carefully measured—during daylight hours—the elevation above the waterline of the boat at full speed, and then measured the space between the surface of the water and the bottom of the railway swing bridge at the Narrows, and determined that we could—if we removed the stern pole light—blast through the Narrows at full speed with fourteen inches to spare under the closed railway swing bridge. We successfully managed the high-speed passage three times, each run smooth and undetected, although on the last transit we forgot to remove the stern light and it was smoothly decapitated. Nobody ever said hormonal teenaged boys—or for that matter, young Maple Leafs hockey players with fat contracts—were practical, wise, or safety-minded.

That was the last summer Paul and I hung out together. We pretty much lost touch with one another after that, what with me away at university and working at various newspapers in the summers in between, and my parents retiring and moving away. In the end, the friendship provided me with at least one valuable life lesson and, curiously, something of incalculable value from my father.

The life lesson learned had to do with drinking. Or rather, learning how not to drink.

We were fifteen at the time and neither of us liked beer, the beverage of choice of everyone we knew. We felt left out. We decided we had to learn how to drink alcohol, so we hunted through bartenders' books at the Mariposa library seeking a recipe that could be replicated from what was on hand in our parents' liquor cabinets.

Ladies and gentleman, may we present . . . The Mariposa Zombie.

Depending on what recipe you used, a Zombie was either four kinds of rum—light, dark, golden, and 151 proof—with some lime and pineapple juices and sugar and a cherry, or else several kinds of rum mixed together with something called grenadine plus orange juice and a cherry. Every Zombie recipe seemed to insist on the cherry.

We knew our family liquor cabinets could yield at least three kinds of rum—light, dark, and Pusser's (or traditional Navy)—so Zombies it would be. We set about liberating a few ounces each of the necessary ingredients and we agreed to sneak out late on a Friday night and meet up on the railway tracks where we'd mix the ingredients and see what it was like to drink grown-up alcohol.

I snuck out toting quantities of dark and Pusser's rum, plus several ounces of rye whiskey because it looked to be the same colour as golden rum ought to be. Paul was supposed to bring the light rum but found out his dad didn't have any, so he brought bourbon he'd mixed with vodka because vodka had no colour and was apparently tasteless. He was supposed to bring the fruit juices, but he couldn't find any in the fridge, so he brought two bottles of cream soda, a drink that was red and fruity looking and, as a bonus, carbonated. He also brought a jar of maraschino cherries.

Out on the tracks under a starry sky, we mixed everything together—including the entire jar of the festive cherries. We toasted our debonair sophistication, drank it all down in less than ten minutes and then settled back on the rail bed to discuss the higher aspects of life and consider what effects the alcohol might have.

It wasn't long before I realized something was happening in my stomach. There was—oh, I don't know—a certain minor rumbling sensation. A growing tightness in the throat and diaphragm. I couldn't feel my feet. I began to sweat and feel generally unwell.

I found myself on my knees, gripping the rail for dear life.

I registered that Paul was next to me, laid out horizontally and apparently suffering from convulsions, but I was concentrating on the flames that seemed to be licking every nerve in my body as an overwhelming numbness took hold of my limbs.

I opened my mouth to say something about something when everything I'd eaten or drunk that day—my mother's bologna casserole, chocolate cake, bits of apple from the afternoon, a reservoir of fermented cream soda—came bursting out of my mouth as if a dam had let go. Seconds later, Paul opened up next to me. Even though it was dark and the contents of his stomach owed a great deal to its liquid base, it was obvious he'd had Salisbury steak with peas and potatoes and pie for dessert.

Zombies did not appear to be our drink.

We lay there for a long time, boneless and vibrating, unable to speak, unable to move. Eventually we were able to stand on rubber legs and totter back to our respective cabins.

I spent the rest of the night in bed in abject awfulness. Every time I closed my eyes, the world would spin horribly. It was worse than the projectile vomiting.

A valuable life lesson was learned. Since that night, I have resolutely avoided drinking more than three glasses of anything alcoholic. At least not in under ten minutes.

And never—ever!—mix alcohol and cream soda.

The other thing my friendship with Paul gained me was the trust of my father.

It happened when Paul and I were kids in grade three and my parents were away at some distant family obligation. Although it was approaching Christmas, the lake had yet to freeze.

Anticipation of freeze-up is difficult to explain to anyone who hasn't been a small boy on a small lake and experienced the glory of a freshly frozen surface, the kind where you could hit a puck and see it slide close to a mile, or skate in a single direction for as long as you wanted and not get anywhere, or stay out on the ice for hours on aching ankles and not feel the need to come in.

Perfect freeze-ups were rare. Most years the lake would freeze during a windless snowfall, or the ice would be too thin to support your weight before it was buried under a blizzard of snowdrifts. In those years, you'd shovel your little rink in front of your house or frequent Angus's larger and better rink a half mile away, and it was fine but rarely was it exhilarating. It was skating on a rink. It was life lived within boundaries.

It was the second-to-last day of school before the Christmas break and the weather was finally promising. A deep and bitter cold enveloped the town. Exhaust plumes from autos and chimneys rose vertically into a windless sky and the lake lay steaming at the foot of the town.

The next morning found me on the shore before school, marvelling at a mirrored surface that stretched four miles across the lake and ten miles down its length.

Experiments were called for.

First, pebbles were sent skittering across the surface. Larger stones were hefted and thrown straight down to produce cracks and fissures and the delightful *ponk* that reverberated away under the ice.

Finally, the bravery test.

I took a few ginger steps out onto the lake, attempting to be as weightless as possible before scrambling back to shore. The ice groaned but held. No water welled up from hairline cracks. With the cloudless skies, the temperature fifteen degrees below freezing, I knew it would thicken throughout the day and be strong enough to skate on after school.

The last day of school before Christmas break seemed endless, with its lessons and carols and cards and the making of tree decorations from coloured paper, doilies, and short lengths of red and green wool. Finally, the bell sounded and Paul and I blew through the doors and ran and laughed all the way home. In our boathouse, we tied up our skates over extra socks, pulled toques over our heads, wobbled to the ice with our hockey sticks and puck, and stood staring at the ice.

What if it was too thin? What if one of us fell through and drowned? What would we tell our parents?

Paul, always more adventuresome, launched himself onto the ice. A few tentative strides, a shout, and he was away.

I followed.

We hugged the shoreline at first, whooping and swooping and sprinting and making short passes with the puck and tearing forward on solo breakaways to nowhere. An errant pass sent the puck five hundred yards out toward the middle of the lake. We skated gingerly after it.

The first foray away from land is always the scariest. The water wasn't deep, but the mental safety of the shore was gone and the colour of the ice was different. Close to shore it's clear and you could see everything on the bottom—sand, rocks, weeds, clams, dead crayfish lying on their backs. But where the water deepened, the ice took on an ominous dark green. You felt yourself suspended over the depths.

The ice held. We retrieved the puck, forgot about our fears, and skated farther out on the lake with the confidence of two junior Jesuses.

The wind, scarcely noticeable near shore, was stiff in the middle of the lake and growing stronger. Our cheeks reddened, our fingers and ears froze, but the exhilaration of the day overcame the physical discomfort. To stop was unthinkable.

Paul did stop briefly but it was only to remove a roll of cloth from his oversized outer pocket. It was one of his mother's linen sheets. He grinned and began to tie it to his hockey stick. I did the same with my stick. We held our sticks aloft and the makeshift sail took us downwind toward Chief Island. We decided to check out the wreck of the *Miss Mariposa* on the far side of the island before it got too dark.

The tour boat *Miss Mariposa* had sunk three years earlier, although "sunk" is a relative term. The boat's owner—a relative of Harold Bolland—had been thinking of retiring and, having kept up his insurance premiums for many years, felt his custom and patronage were owed formal recognition. He decided to perform a variation on the maritime practice—begun millennia before in the Mediterranean and perfected in the twentieth century by the seagoing folks of the West Indies—called "letting her go."

If you were, say, the owner of a West Indian commercial skiff whose hull was failing and soon to be rendered useless for commercial business, you'd contract to take a load of valuable goods—bricks, for instance, or tiles, or concrete blocks—from one island to another. During passage between the islands— usually at the deepest point of the transit—the sea cocks would mysteriously open, or the hull would hit something mysterious—an axe head, maybe—and the craft would sink. That's called "letting her go." At least that's what it was called outside an insurer's office. The insurance industry has another name for it.

Thus it was on a stormy day that the operator of the *Miss Mariposa* took a fishing party—consisting of those members

of his extended family who could swim—over to the far side
of Chief Island. It was a locale not notable for its fishing but,
interestingly, it was the only place on the lake that could not
be seen from a populated shoreline.

The next day, the *Mariposa Daily Packet & Times* carried a
front-page story about the dramatic sinking of the *Miss Mariposa*
and how the engine had quit, and how large waves had
washed over the side of the helpless craft, and how the terrified
fishing party struggled to bail against the rising waters, and
how everyone escaped unscathed thanks to another boat that
happened to be passing and whose skipper saw the tragedy
unfolding and daringly hove to and took everyone off to safety
and the comfort of their loved ones.

The newspaper account failed to mention that the operator
of the other craft was the brother-in-law of *Miss Mariposa*'s
operator or to offer any explanation as to why he was out braving
the elements and stormy waters himself. It was enough that
the Mariposa fire chief—a friend of Mr. Bolland—cited the skipper
for "action, gallantry, bravery, and quick-thinking heroics."

Paul and I stared down at the sunken boat. It lay beneath
our feet under the transparent ice like a giant model in a bottle.
Really, really neat.

It was getting dark, so we began the long skate home. It was
hard slogging with the wind in our faces and I was skating with
my head down when I glimpsed something white under the ice.
I kept skating while the white image rattled around my head,
trying to connect with something. The shape was familiar but
out of place.

I circled back, the wind pushing me along, until I spotted
the white shape again.

Dropping to my knees, I tried to peer through the ice, cupping
my hands around my eyes like a boy trying to look through
a window into a dim store. The image was blurred so close to

the ice, so I stood up again and the image came into focus and registered.

I screamed for Paul to come back, continuing to stare down at the white shape.

Paul skated back to ask what's the matter. I gestured below our feet and said, "Look what I found!"

Paul looked down, stared a second or two, then whooped.

We were standing above a sunken aircraft.

I was one of those kids who knew everything about the float planes that used our lake and I could tell this one was a four-seater Cessna 172. It was resting nose-down at a 45-degree angle. The protruding vertical stabilizer—the tail fin—was a few feet below the ice but the fuselage—and the registration letters that would be on it—was lost in the depths and the failing light.

"Do you think anyone's in it?" Paul asked.

The thought hadn't occurred to me. We tried to see if there were any outlines in the rear window but couldn't make anything out. To judge by what we could see, the aircraft hadn't been in the water long. There was no growth on its immaculate red-and-white paint.

"Who we gonna tell first?"

We babbled like idiots. It was the most righteous outstanding discovery imaginable. Almost as good as treasure. An airplane in the lake and we found it! Maybe there's a reward! Maybe there's dead people inside! Maybe there's dead people and a treasure and a reward!

Lights in the gathering dark now marked the shoreline, more than a mile away. Taking the brightest as our marks, we fixed our location with cross points on the shore before starting for home. We didn't mind the cold wind. The excitement of the find kept us warm. We didn't pay attention to the snow that had begun to blow under our feet.

An hour later I was lying on my bed, fighting back tears.

My grandmother didn't believe me! My own grandmother didn't believe me! The very best kind of discovery and my grandmother thinks I'm making it up because I was late for her macaroni casserole.

There is nothing madder or more petulant than a kid who thinks he's been wronged.

In retrospect, it was understandable. My mother's mother was a tough egg, a prairie widow who'd raised nine kids in Moose Jaw during the Depression, the type that viewed the presence of a box of cornflakes in our house as evidence of backsliding, and when she filled in for my parents—as she was doing—she made sure there was hot porridge—and only hot porridge—on the breakfast table. She wasn't taking any story about an airplane under the ice as any excuse for tardiness to the dinner table.

And in truth, from time to time, I had been known to exaggerate. To unduly extend reality. To embellish a fact.

Take the matter of our fish.

Each year, a very large bass—whom we called Billy—made a nest in the gravel beneath the end of our dock and kept a fierce vigil over its eggs. If you were slow to get in or get out of the water on the swimming ladder, Billy would ram your ankle with a force you had to experience to believe. It was my job to protect Billy from the interest or attention of passing fishermen.

In response to a "Recount an interesting animal story!" oral assignment in school, I told the class about our pet fish, Billy the Bass. I felt the story wasn't going over with the class, so I added an, um, embellishment to get their attention and make them sit up and take notice. I said that Billy would come to you if you blew a special whistle.

This whopper quickly got back to my parents. I received a lecture on the necessity of telling the truth, and the incident was forgotten. Dropped. Never spoken of again. Unless by forgotten or dropped or never spoken of again you mean it was embraced, enjoyed, and enshrined forever in family lore. Neighbourhood lore, too, and possibly even municipal lore, but I digress.

The phone rang while I was moping in bed. I leapt up and raced downstairs to the hallway to get it before my grandmother could. It was Paul. He was wailing. His parents didn't believe him either.

This, at least, made sense. I might be an exaggerator, but Paul had a seriously active imagination. Unexplained events in his telling tended to be the work of saboteurs. Or squads of trained killer scuba divers. Or Martians. Small wonder his parents weren't buying a plane under the ice.

What to do? My parents weren't due home until the day before Christmas and somebody might find the airplane before then. Somebody might steal our glory.

We have to go to the police, I said. Next morning, that's what we did.

The desk sergeant had a problem. Here were two kids with an outlandish story about an aircraft under the ice when there were no reports of a missing aircraft. They are the sons of two prominent Mariposa fathers, one of them publisher of the local newspaper. Desk sergeants, however, are wise and cautious by nature and by practice, so he told us he'd take down our information and then we'd better skedaddle.

My parents returned home on Christmas Eve day and I told them the story over dinner. They listened but seemed skeptical, especially as the story involved Paul and I doing something together. Separately, we were story enhancers. Together? Well, who knows?

Finally my father leaned over the table and said in a very low voice, "Is this on the level?"

I assured him it was.

Okay, he said. He'd look into it. For now, though, he wanted everything normal. We read the usual Christmas Eve stories and hung our stockings and put out the milk and cookies, but my heart wasn't in it. Even the loot the next morning, and the unique rush a kid gets when he sees Santa has knocked back the milk and cookies left by the chimney, wasn't as exciting as it would normally be. The thrill just wasn't there.

My mother, accustomed to me fizzing like a seltzer tablet on Christmas Day, noticed my flatness. She and my father had a little talk in the den. My father spent nearly an hour on the phone.

In the afternoon, he told me to dress warmly. We were going on a search.

Two hours later, Paul and I led a group of adults to the spot where we thought we'd seen the aircraft. The group included my dad, Paul's dad, two cops, two divers toting their equipment, and a couple of printers from the newspaper equipped with ice saws.

It had taken us some time to arrive at what might be the right place. It was a sunny day, but the ice was blanketed with snow and there were no reference lights on the shore.

Paul and I were both nervous. My father wasn't saying anything, but he'd put his reputation on the line. If we didn't find anything, life was going to be pretty miserable around the house. Paul's father looked like a storm cloud.

We finally made an X with our boots in the snow, declared it to be the spot, and the printers began sawing a hole in the ice while the divers suited up. They dropped a couple of yellow ropes into the hole and, after spitting loudly into their masks, lowered themselves beneath the ice.

We waited. Minutes ticked by. Five. Ten. Fifteen. The tension was awful. Maybe this wasn't the spot. Maybe we didn't see what we thought we saw. All sorts of doubts and fears rose up to assail us.

Finally, a diver came up, lifted his mask, and said his air was about up. He had found nothing. A few minutes later, the other diver appeared. He didn't say anything as he crawled out on the ice and took off his mask.

He stared at us. He didn't look happy. Our hearts were in our boots.

The diver spoke.

"I found it," he said. "Just like the kids here said. It's a Cessna 172. There's two dead men in the cockpit. Been there a couple of days by the looks of it."

The adults looked grim. Dead men under the ice was a sobering thought. For adults.

For us, it was vindication. We practically danced. See? We found it! We told you it was here and it's here!

Looking back, the event changed my life. Not in any dramatic fashion with rewards or local prestige—the newspaper story simply said a Toronto aircraft was found by some kids and that an investigation was under way—but in a small and subtle fashion that rippled through my life down to the present day.

My parents—my father in particular—had believed me. When everything told them not to, they believed me. My father had put his reputation on the line for me. I didn't think much of it at the time, but I do now. Especially when my own kids would come and tell me something outlandish.

Paul and I might be separated by decades of life and experience, but we're bound by that day. By all our days. Bound as all childhood friends are bound.

By joy. By friendship. And by the occasional game of sticks.

The Mariposa Belle

NEXT TO THE Donald house is a two-storey house obscured from the street by a large garage. These buildings replaced the small white house built for two elderly ladies named Miss Dean and Miss Railley on land that used to be part of our property.

My father sold this land to the two retired nurses because it tickled him to do so. As my mother explained it to me after my father's death, a businessman was bugging my father to sell him this part of our property so he could build a big house for himself on the water. "The man was offering $10,000," she said. "That was a lot of money in those days, more than twice what your father was making a year, but your father didn't like the idea of some big house going up next to us, and he certainly didn't like the idea of having this man as our neighbour."

My father happened to talk with Doc Hipwell, who said there were these retired nurses—"two lovely old dears"—who wanted to spend their remaining days on the lake but didn't have much money and weren't having any luck finding a house, or a year-round rental, or a building lot. My father invited the two spinsters to lunch, liked them immediately, and offered to hive off a half-acre chunk of our property for them to build a little house on, so long as the house was set back from the water to preserve everyone's view. He sold the half-acre of waterfront property to them for less than a thousand dollars.

A local builder, who worshipped Miss Dean and Miss Railley for their care and kindnesses to a dying mother, built them a trim and tidy little white house in less than three months. Total cost of house and waterfront property—five thousand dollars.

Anyone buying on the waterside of Bay Street today is a millionaire by definition, and while there were some wealthy people on the street when I lived here, most were retired or working middle class. That would describe our family's situation, although my dad's occupation elevated our social standing. I earned more in my first year as a reporter for the *Vancouver Sun* than my publisher-and-editor father earned in his best year. How well you lived in Mariposa was not dependent on what you earned.

Miss Dean and Miss Railley were wonderful neighbours. They'd eschewed a heating system in favour of an old wood stove in the kitchen that did double duty as cooker and house heater. Winter and summer, the cast iron monster was throwing off heat, and once a week either Paul or I or both of us would tote wood from their garage—cords of which were deposited by a woodlot owner the ladies had nursed back to health—up to the kitchen. We'd perch on kitchen chairs, swinging our legs, soaking up the aroma of fresh baked bread while waiting for the Chelsea buns to cool enough so we could slather them with butter and eat them off faded china plates.

Meanwhile, Paul and I treated the ladies' waterfront lawn as a thoroughfare between our houses, using holes in our respective hedges for entrance and egress.

After Miss Dean passed away, followed by Miss Railley a few months later, the house was sold to the Tryon family. Mr. Tryon was not enamoured of his lawn being used as a passageway by two small boys, and he warned us that the Tryon family dog—an enormous Newfoundland, a breed bred to haul fishing nets and carts—would be living outdoors all year round and should be kept away from because Mr. Tryon said he couldn't answer for the dog's protective instincts and aggressive actions toward trespassers.

The dog's name was Ben and he made himself a cave in the hedge a dozen feet from the hole on Paul's side of the yard. For weeks, Paul and I avoided passage across the Tryon lakefront lawn, but one afternoon, not seeing Ben anywhere in the yard, we decided to be brave and made a dash across the grass. In a single bounding flash, Ben appeared before us, blocking our way to the hedge hole. We were all of the same height, so Ben's brown eyes were level with—and locked on to—ours.

We stood frozen, afraid to move.

"Lie down," Paul hissed. I thought he was hissing at the dog, but it turned out he was hissing an order to me. "Get down on the ground. Ready? One. Two. Three."

Paul and I sank to our knees. Ben didn't move.

"Now lie down," Paul said.

We did.

Ben cocked his head, regarded us for a moment, then ambled his bulk over and lay down between us. Pretty soon we were patting him and stroking his thick fur and the three of us were rolling around together on the ground.

After that, Ben would come out and escort us across the Tryon lawn, making sure that our skis or lunch boxes or comic books or concealed *Playboys*—whatever we were carrying—were safe while on his turf. I don't think Mr. Tryon was happy about it, but what could he do? The big burly Newfie was protecting his people.

Mr. and Mrs. Tryon's son, Vic, was the human equivalent of Ben the Newfoundland. Big, intimidating until you got to know him, ultimately good-natured and affable, Vic was a little older than us and an athlete, so we didn't hang out much. Paul and I, however, did get a ride to school every day with him and his dad. We'd wait next to the car and Vic would emerge from the house, yank your shirt out of your pants, slap you on the stomach, punch you on the shoulder, cuff the back of your head, ruffle your combed hair. That was just Vic's way of saying good morning.

My parents had already moved to Cape Breton when the Tryons moved out and a new owner pulled down Miss Dean and Miss Railley's bargain home and put up the present view-blocker, but I couldn't care less because now I'm already looking at the next house along—or what little of it I can see over the hedge—because this had been our house.

My father bought it—the house, the one-and-a-half acres of waterfront property, plus the empty lot across the street by the railway tracks—for thirteen thousand dollars.

Jesus, God, it was another time.

Here's a description of my house, written by my father.

When we had first come to Mariposa, my wife and I had found a dream house, a real never-never-land sort of place, nestled on the shore of Lake Wissanotti, and bought it on the spot at the sort of give-away price which today seems so unbelievable. Covered in dark-brown cedar shingles, crowned with a soft-rose roof with a distinctive upturning eave line that imparted a faintly Oriental touch, it had leaded lattice windows that looked out on long lawns that sloped down to the lake on both sides. Clumps of birch, maple, willow, and blue spruce were dominated by an enormous oak. Scattered around inside the cedar hedges were a garage, a tiny guest-house with its own facilities, a long asphalt drive, a couple of patios, an old stone fireplace with flagstone walks and steps leading nowhere in particular, and a grassy terrace under the oak with magnificent views across the lake, where our cannon, a little one-and-a-half pound cannonade that had once served in Nelson's navy as a boat gun, peered defiantly out over the water.

The house reeked of character; it had been built from the timbers of the old steamer Geneva, and when we undertook a few alterations we discovered the massive pitch-pine timbers of the old ship underneath, still with their white and red paint, together with the oak tongue-and-groove sheathing from the steamer's interior that lined the walls. There was a dry boathouse underneath, an attic that converted into a separate sanctum for the boy upstairs, and a domed living room roughly the size of Toronto's Union Station looking out over the lake through one of Mariposa's first picture windows.

With its detached air, of being separate and distinct from the workaday world outside, it was enchanted and enchanting, the stuff of dreams. We called it "Mariposa," had its name cut into the red granite gatepost, and lived there in blissful happiness for more than twenty years.

My father made no secret of the house being built from the timbers of the *Geneva* but he never wrote or spoke in public about the *Geneva* being the model for Leacock's *Mariposa Belle*. Which is odd. He knew the real identity of the *Mariposa Belle* yet was content to let the matter remain a public mystery.

Scholars examining the tea leaves of Leacock's life and writings were never able to settle on the identity of the model for the *Mariposa Belle,* the author's most famous creation. Was it the lake steamer *Longford*? Some said it was the *Geneva*. A Lake Ossawippi steamer—the *Enterprise*—was in the mix because it once sank at its moorings in shallow water, and many plumped for the steamer *Islay* because it fit the general description and was popular for marine outings of the type Leacock ascribed to his Knights of Pythias. Unable to authoritatively pin the tail on a single steamer, the consensus academic opinion was that Leacock had fashioned the *Mariposa Belle* from a combination of lake steamers.

There was no need for consensus opinion from the locals, however. They knew which steamer was the *Mariposa Belle*, but being locals—unconcerned about the true identity of a steamer in a book and thus unable to appreciate the higher forms of learning—they were never asked. Or in the case of my father, or the old *Packet* editor C.H. Kale, they provided wishy-washy replies that neither confirmed nor denied the academic reasoning.

But they knew. A lot of people knew. People such as Mrs. Dorothy Spicer and her husband, Jack, who were my parent's best friends in Mariposa. Mrs. Spicer's maiden name was Tudhope and she was the daughter of the town's biggest industrialist. More important, she was one of the girls Stephen Leacock invited to Brewery Bay to take part in the little pageants and Christmas plays he wrote so that son Stevie—sickly, isolated, and therefore friendless—could play with local kids his age and have something to perform in. Dorothy's father had read her the chapter in *Sunshine Sketches* on the sinking of the *Mariposa Belle* as a bedtime story—laughing loudly as he did so—and Dorothy, being a precocious child, asked the author if it was still possible to take an excursion on the *Mariposa Belle*.

"No, dear," Leacock told her. "The steamer was frozen in the ice, taken apart, and now she's part of the canoe club over on Bay Street."

The capper, though, came from Fred Terigo, an old compositor at the *Mariposa Daily Packet & Times* and a great favourite of my father. In his youth, Freddy had been Leacock's yard boy at Brewery Bay, and he would describe how he used to sit on the veranda and listen to Leacock tell stories to his son, Stevie.

"Young Stevie was sick on the day bed and Mister Leacock would make up these stories—real good yarns, they were—and I used to sit outside the window and listen to them. I remember how the cheesecloth—Mister Leacock didn't have screens in then—would bulge in and out of the window in the breeze."

One day, "a fella" came to the Leacock house lugging a piece of machinery. Freddy escorted him around the house to where Leacock was working in one of the gardens.

"Fella said he remembered how Mister Leacock had asked the guys who were stripping out the *Geneva* if there was a little piece of the ship he could have," Freddie said. "'Well,' the fella said, 'Here it is.' Mister Leacock looks at this iron contraption and says, 'What the hell is it?' Fella says, 'It's the *Geneva*'s hand pump. Remember how you wrote about her sinking and how the bandsmen used the hand pump in the bow of the lower decks to pump her out? Well, here it is.'"

"Mister Leacock stared at the fella," Freddie said. "He said, 'I was thinking of something small from the pilot house. Something brass. Like a porthole.' And then Mister Leacock threw back his head and laughed, and thanked the fella for the pump anyway."

Years later, Dr. Ralph Furry—Leacock biographer, first curator of the Leacock home/museum, professor, and possessor of a barking laugh and outrageous Kentucky accent—was standing around talking with my father after we'd hauled Leacock's old fishing punt out of the mud and left it on the Leacock home's lawn to dry. (The Leacock Board had been thinking of spending money to construct a replica of Leacock's fishing boat and my dad had said, "Why? The real one's sunk in mud up to the gunnels five feet offshore." With me as cheap labour, we'd arrived unannounced and hauled Leacock's punt out of the mud for inspection by the bemused curator.)

Dr. Furry, a regular visitor to our house, thanked us for our questionable efforts and, by way of showing the museum's gratitude, said they were in the process of chucking a lot of unusable and useless junk out of one of the old garden sheds and would we be interested in any of it. We walked over and admired a shed containing one or two of the great man's rusty garden implements and dozens of rusty paint cans and mouldering bits of wood and were about to leave when my father noticed—tucked behind a broken trellis on the dirt floor—a piece of rusting cast metal machinery. He went over and looked at it.

"Ralph," he said. "Do you know what this is?"

Dr. Furry came over, peered at the offensive item with its chambers and pistons, and said no, he didn't know what it was.

"It's a pump," my dad said. "It's missing all its hoses and its wooden handle, but it's a marine pump. Pretty sure it's off one of the old lake steamers. Pretty sure it's off the *Geneva*."

Dr. Furry allowed as how that was nice, and how typical of my father to spot something of a marine nature in a gardening shed—our house being plastered with naval prints and littered with all things nautical, including the ship's wheel and ship's bell from HMCS *Minas*, a Canadian minesweeper and my father's first wartime command—and if my father liked the pump so much, why, he was welcome to it because otherwise it was going to the dump, and how about a little snifter of road-straightener before you go?

I was ordered to horse the thing out of the shed and across the yard to the trunk of our car while the two of them shared a shot of Kentucky bourbon in the museum office. My father bubbled all the way home. In the weeks to come, he had someone sandblast the metal, paint it in fire-engine red enamel, and lathe and varnish a wooden handle and insert it in place. He hung a little flowerpot off each arm and placed it up against the house between our two front doors—under the ship's bell—where it remained for more than a decade. Any time a puzzled visitor asked what this extraordinary plant holder was, my father said, "Oh, it's an old marine pump. Terrific, isn't it?" Our friends and neighbours knew what it was—and what it signified—but nobody said a word to the Leacock folks about it.

In the days when he knew he was dying, my father and I were walking and talking about things that matter, and I asked him why he never spoke of the *Geneva* being the model for the *Mariposa Belle*.

"When we first moved in, the old-timers on the lake all knew the story of how the house had first been the Mariposa Canoe Club, and how the club came to be built out of materials from the *Geneva*, and how and why they'd made Leacock an honorary member of the club, and it wasn't a big deal. But when the Leacock movement really got rolling, preserving everything, playing up the Leacock name, putting up historic plaques on anything to do with Leacock—all efforts I was proud to be part of, you understand—I realized what could happen. I didn't want some government functionary erecting a plaque at the top of our driveway to say that the house on the lake you see before you today was constructed from the timbers of the vessel that was the inspiration for the *Mariposa Belle*. They'd probably have expropriated part of our property so cars could pull off to the side and gawk at us. Plain and simple, I didn't want them putting their mitts on our house."

"It was," he said, "too special a place for that."

He's right. It was. Maybe still is, although there's really nothing left to see or anyone left alive to authenticate the link between an author and a lake steamer and a house on Bay Street.

The silhouette of the house is generally the same, but the exterior wooden shingles have been replaced with stone, the two front doors are now one, there's been some modest additions and a new roof added, the inside has been pretty much gutted and altered—the ship's beams covered up, the panelling removed—and the lakeside frontage is flat-out unrecognizable. A subsequent owner took the marine pump from where it sat outdoors and did what the Leacock museum originally intended to do. He took it to the dump.

There is, quite simply, nothing on or in the house to connect it to its origin anymore.

There had been one thing—call it an artefact—but it's not on Bay Street anymore. It's 3,300 kilometres away in a house outside Vancouver, but it had been resident here for the span of our family's occupancy and the canoe club's before us. We inherited it when the club was converted to a house—our house—and its significance explained by an old club member to my father, who proudly displayed it on his grandfather's desk, itself an original desk from the council chamber of the original Toronto city hall, but really, the artefact seemed part of the general nautical clutter of my father's den.

It's a porthole.

A brass porthole.

The glass is cracked and backed with old blue paper and the brass is tarnished and a little pitted, but the large locking screw still works and the port still opens and closes firmly. In the centre of the glass port is taped a small postcard. The postcard is a black-and-white photo postcard of a lake steamer. The steamer is flying its flags and pennants. Its decks are lined with formally dressed people. You can see the ship's nameplate on the bow at just about the place you'd find a hand pump. The printed caption on the postcard reads, "The *Geneva* on Lake Wissanotti."

My great grandfather's Toronto council chamber desk is now in my house, although I don't use it much, the long table being so handy and better suited for a computer. But propped up on a shelf in the floor-to-ceiling bookcase—amid books by Leacock and S.J. Perelman and P.G. Wodehouse and Douglas

Adams—is the porthole, the artefact Leacock had sought as a memento of a lake steamer that had plied the waters around the little town in the sunshine he knew.

Home for Christmas

ORGET ABOUT THE *Mariposa Belle*. Forget about what this place looks like now or what it used to look like. Focus instead on what it represents.

For me, it represents home. Or at least, the idea of home.

To a kid, home is what's familiar. It is a geography of familiar surroundings populated by familiar people doing familiar things.

It doesn't matter if you grew up in one house or a dozen, you learned the layout of your surroundings and that was your physical world. You learned early on who the people were around you, and what their routine was with regard to you, and that filled up the geography and made it home.

For the longest time, you never judged it. Your life was as it presented itself to you, no questions asked of the geography or the people, no judgements rendered. It stayed that way until you had something else to compare it to, something that jiggled the picture and shifted your eyes and brain into seeing something different, something that said maybe your house, maybe the members of your family, maybe your neighbourhood, maybe your life wasn't the same as everyone else's. That maybe you're not the norm. That maybe you're an exception.

Not exceptional. Not better than. Not worse than. Just a little . . . different.

My family was different. I had no idea how much.

I first saw it in the little things. I'd go over to Paul's and he'd fetch us a snack from his fridge. Our fridge didn't have anything remotely resembling a snack, unless you count eating a strip of uncooked bacon. Snacks were not in my family's vocabulary. We ate three meals a day and that was that. My mother knew to the individual slice how much baloney or cheese or bread was in the house, and she was the sole dispenser. But open Paul's fridge and there were actual store-bought items on offer, ready to go. Sliced meats that you could pair with strange mustards and Miracle Whip and real butter and real milk. We had French's mustard and homemade mayonnaise—made from a tin of condensed milk—and the kind of white margarine you had to knead with a little gel cap of red dye to colour it, which my mother did while watching television. And we had powdered milk.

Jesus, powdered milk! Was there anything worse? Occasionally we had the Carnation stuff, itself pretty awful but you could at least drink it without heroics, but my mother favoured an inexpensive powdered milk mix called Milko. You added water and stirred it to produce a yellowish mix of unappetizing lumps and curds that was undrinkable if you possessed a gag reflex. I believe they still use the stuff for cattle in the poorer sections of central Europe and Africa.

Paul's mom bought homogenized milk, which to me was like drinking Devon cream. Mrs. Donald also bought potato chips and little cupcakes and single-portion confections filled with artificial cream and fruit-flavoured sugars and a long list of preservatives neither healthy nor nutritious and entirely wonderful. She also stocked Coke and Pepsi and Fizzies, all the sugar and empty calories a growing boy could want on a hot summer's day.

It was the snacks that got me thinking, were we poor? I wasn't sure what poor was, but I was pretty sure it included drinking powdered milk and eating apples instead of store-bought milk and apple turnovers out of a package. On the other hand, poor people probably didn't have a canoe and a sailboat and a little outboard cruiser that was pulled out of the lake at night on a motorized marine railroad and deposited in the boathouse in the basement of their house. Or a cannon on their lawn. Or a flagpole that flew the red ensign during the summer, the white ensign on Battle of the Atlantic Sunday, the Union Jack on the Queen's birthday, and the French tri-colour on Bastille Day.

Rich or poor, I'm pretty sure no other Mariposa kid had their father precede a weekly inspection of his room by blowing a bosun's pipe and declaring, "All hands, fall in for inspection!" Or be called home for dinner by the ringing of a ship's bell that could be heard a mile away.

No, not poor. Just naval. And budget conscious. My mother fed us on a very strict budget, with any surplus going toward the family vacation.

In our house, the word "family" paired with the word "vacation" meant a vacation for my parents, and only my parents. It took me a while to appreciate that their concept of vacation meant getting away from the daily routine and I was part of the daily routine that needed getting away from.

My parents had two two-week vacations each year. The first involved my dad taking his two weeks off work in mid- to late winter and travelling to islands in the West Indies that hadn't then been discovered by the masses—Tobago and Saint Lucia and Saint Vincent and Bequia—where they'd stay in tiny inns and six-room hotels. Sometimes they'd go with Mr. and Mrs. Spicer. One time, the couples chartered a decrepit little schooner. Mr. Spicer and my dad took turns spelling the owner to pilot the boat themselves under equatorial constellations and tropical moons and an experience that in Mrs. Spicer's words "turned these two pillars of Mariposa society into a couple of ten-year-old boys." Wherever they went, my parents always returned tanned and happy and affectionate with one another.

I once asked if I could go south to the West Indies with them. My father fielded the question in the manner of an asylum counsellor responding to an inmate's silly request. Why would anyone want to go to the sweaty old tropics with their parents—their *parents,* of all people—when they could be in Mariposa and playing in the crisp and healthy sub-zero outdoors or tucked up at home, all warm and toasty and doing beneficial and life-enhancing homework and eating freshly boiled porridge under the watchful eye of their ninety-year-old prairie grandmother?

Their two-week summer vacation was a different matter. My dad didn't take time off work and they didn't officially go anywhere.

I did.

For two weeks in the summer. To the YMCA camp on the other side of the lake.

The moment I left and the all-clear was sounded, my folks would begin taking little day trips up the lake in the sailboat and overnight trips along the river-and-lock system in the little cruiser and spend an early morning or two on the golf course— climbing the fence, playing three or four holes beneath the hill where they couldn't be seen from the clubhouse, then climbing back over the fence to their getaway car—and afternoons lounging on the patio or sunning on the raft or taking their gin-and-tonics and a leisurely dinner on the boat in the lee of Chief Island, all of it while I was interned in a cabin in a POW camp.

Well, camp wasn't strictly terrible. The YMCA tried hard. There was softball and swimming and canoeing and horse-shoes and games of Capture the Flag but I couldn't see the point. I could have done all these things across the lake at home, with the added bonus of sailing and waterskiing and sleeping in my own personal cabin. Instead, I got to enjoy the company of two hundred boys all doing the same thing at the same time: viz., taking pointless hikes and mindless nature walks on sunny days and crafting bracelets out of pre-cut lengths of plastic string on the rainy ones, to say nothing of daily use of the camp's ancient multi-hole outdoor toilets named "Turtle's Grave" and "Rotary Roost." The latter—a six-holer—was named for the Mariposa service organization that dug the trench and put up the wooden building three decades earlier. The name of the former—a two-holer—doesn't bear thinking about.

I was at camp on the day the president of the Mariposa Rotary Club came to visit his son and had occasion to make use of the facility named in honour of his club. When he emerged, expelling the breath he'd held for nearly five minutes, he was a changed man. Shaken, you might say, if his skin shade—an attractive light green, edged with blue—was anything to go by. He immediately ordered the camp to paint out the club's name on the faded sign on the roof, leaving only the word "Roost." A camp counsellor later climbed up on the roof with a spray can and altered the five-letter word—changing the "R" into a "P" and painting out the "st"—to a three-letter word that succinctly summed up the facility's purpose.

Summer camp was a terrific thing for a great many kids—it got them into and onto the water, and that's no small thing. The Mariposa YMCA is justly celebrated for it, but for me, who already spent every day of every year on or next to the lake, all camp did was make me appreciate home.

Not just in summer but in all seasons. Spring, summer, fall, all of them superb, but really my entire year was a buildup to the big day of the year, the happiest day of the year, a day freighted with family tradition—Christmas Day.

Every family builds its own traditions, things they come to do a certain way on a certain day. These are not to be confused with family practices, the things a family does with no regard to the day or season and are generally inexplicable to anyone outside the family. Off the top of my head, I can think of two practices in our family that fit that particular bill—the hunting of Stinchcombes and the burying of treasure.

Once, while in the West Indies, my mother met a couple named Stinchcombe. She thought the name was intriguing and asked them where it came from. The couple said it was Brazilian. Two years later, my mother was talking to a waiter in London, discovered his name was Stinchcombe, asked him where the name came from, and he said it was a French Huguenot name. That same trip, she met yet another Stinchcombe on a local train in Scotland, asked him, and he said it was ancient English.

My mother thought the name—and the lack of cohesion in an origin story for the name—was hilarious. She began to look up the name Stinchcombe in phone books wherever she went. Over the years, and particularly the last thirty years of her life when she and my father travelled extensively, she found Stinchcombes littered across the world, including the Azores, the Algarve, and Tangiers. It became a family practice that whenever anyone of us went anywhere, we'd have to check the phone book for Stinchcombes. On travels with the prime minister, I found Stinchcombes in Jakarta, Hong Kong, and Manila.

My father's family practice of burying money around the world began innocently enough when he noticed he had a stash of unused coins from his travels around Europe, the West Indies, and Japan. Too small to be cashed in, the coins were put in a Crown Royal blue velvet bag, wrapped up in waterproof plastic, and buried on one of the small islands at the north end of our lake. He drew a little map of its location—complete with instructions like "Seven paces west from Top Rock"—on the flyleaf of *Sunshine Sketches of a Little Town,* the twenty-five-cent Collins White Circle Pocket Novel edition—and gave the book to me to read. I think he thought the paperback cover—a simple map-like illustration of a few buildings to represent Mariposa and a little paddlewheeler on a lake to represent the *Mariposa Belle*—was in keeping with the map he'd drawn inside, and maybe the treasure map would be an incentive to read what he considered to be a masterpiece.

I did read it. Loved it, in fact. So later that year, Paul and I took his boat up to the island, paced off the instructions, dug up the treasure—X marked the spot—but finding no usable currency for soft drinks or potato chips, we returned the contents to the bag and buried it in the ground where we found it.

After my dad retired, he and my mother would wander Europe, following old Roman roads and hunting Bronze Age barrows and passage graves and hill forts. Anywhere he found a place of historical interest that ticked his three boxes—a great view, a comfortable place to sit, and a nearby pub or place where a couple could buy a drink and a sandwich—he'd bury enough money for lunch and a drink and make a map. He'd give the map to friends who were bound for a vacation in the same area. He must have buried between forty and fifty such treasures in Europe in locales extending from the Shetlands and Orkneys in the north to Malaga and Torres Vedras in the south.

Both family practices came together when my parents visited Stinchcombe Hill—on the edge of the Cotswolds in England, between Dursley and North Nibley—for the express purpose of burying my mother's worldwide list of Stinchcombes and their addresses. "If I ever get to know a Stinchcombe, I'll give them the map, and they can contact one another and argue about what their name means and where it's from," she said.

But as I said, these were family practices, not family traditions. A family's Christmas tradition builds over time. Like a snowflake, no family tradition is the same as another family's tradition.

Some families build the day around a church service. Some build it around the giving and getting of presents. Some build it around family coming to visit or going to visit the family themselves. Still others spend the day ignoring the religion and the presents and the family altogether.

Our traditions were set early on and were the same year after year. To me, they were holiday heroin, and I never got enough of them.

It would begin with the getting of the tree.

For us, it was always a Scotch pine. For most others in Mariposa, too. Scotch pine was a long-needled European variety easily grown in our local woodlots and able to survive whatever the weather and insects threw at them. Those were the days before the coming of the US tree plantations when you got a local tree not as a choice but as a necessity. It was fresh and fragrant and filled the house with that wonderful waxy just-sawed sap smell.

Around the anniversary of Pearl Harbor my father would go out after work to the tree lot operated by the Mariposa Boy Scouts, bring home a tree, drag it into the house, and lay it on the living room carpet in the manner of a caveman exhibiting a fresh kill.

Woman! I am home from the hunt! Prepare the eggnog!

My mother would give him an in-your-dreams look and go back to whatever casserole she happened to be incinerating in the oven.

I should say here that I love my mother, but she was not a wonderful cook. Pretty much everything she made was the product of her Saskatchewan upbringing and the one cookbook she owned, *From Saskatchewan Homemakers' Kitchens*—"A cookbook compiled by Homemakers' Clubs in honor of Saskatchewan's Golden Jubilee." There's not a typed or typeset word in it. The recipes are hand printed or handwritten and they're reproduced in the company of little cartoon drawings of talking hot dogs and dancing pickles and roguish strips of bacon cozying up to smiling fried eggs.

The cookbook opens with this sentence: "Early settlers gave freely of food and hospitality to all who passed by on the prairie trails." My question would be: How many of those "who passed by" would quickly pass away from the food and hospitality? God save Saskatchewan's homemakers, but their locale and their times meant that if a recipe didn't feature flour, lard, and several pounds of sugar and salt, a dish wouldn't make it to the table.

That's a grossly unfair comment, of course. As one of the cookbook's many forewords states, "Since the Jubilee Cook Book has been compiled from recipes which the Saskatchewan Homemakers are actually using in 1955, it is not surprising to find ingredients called for such as pineapple titbits, potato chips, salad oil and commercial pectin." Indeed, "the recipes reflect the influence of modern advertisers and the universal availability of ingredients prepared by modern food technologists."

You bet they do. If it's canned, or can be boiled, it's in this book. Like many of the local or regional cookbooks produced by church groups or women's groups of the era, it's chockablock with main courses that hit the table as casseroles or loaves or as a complete surprise. Tuna Surprise. Liver Surprise. Pineapple Surprise. Anything with pineapple was designated as Hawaiian. My favourite of these never-to-be-cooked recipes was the Hawaian Special [sic] with its three ingredients and one simple instruction—"1 pt. marshmallows, 1 qt. pineapple, and 1 qt. cabbage. Combine."

If I sound as if I'm belittling these dishes or the good folk who contributed them to the cookbook, let me hasten to make amends. My all-time favourite dessert, the one my mother made every year for my birthday at my request, was from this cookbook. It was called Pineapple Dessert and featured vanilla "waffers," butter or margarine—my mother always chose margarine—heaping amounts of confectioner's sugar, two eggs, a tin of crushed pineapple, and a pint of whipping cream. Sweet? It could open cavities at twenty paces, and it kept our dentist in Florida vacations for years. I've kept my mother's cookbook just to have that one recipe, although I've never actually made it myself. It just wouldn't taste the same without the accompaniment of my mother's smile as she brought it to the table for me on my birthday.

Our weekly dinner fare when I was growing up consisted of a series of loafs and casseroles and surprises. There was something called Mock Duck Loaf which featured the toughest cut of beef you could find, wrapped around some sort of bread stuffing, closed with a toothpick, and baked senseless. Her go-to dinner—which we supped upon at least once a week—was a slice of bologna wrapped around something mysterious, doused in ketchup mixed with Worcestershire sauce, affixed with the traditional toothpick, and placed under the broiler for an afternoon until blackened and charred.

She could do a Christmas turkey, though. The vegetables weren't memorable—potatoes and carrots and peas boiled until they were shadows of their former selves—but then their job was to act as something to pour gravy over, and I loved her gravy.

Her pride and joy were her mince tarts, which I'm told were terrific. I never ate one myself. I hated mince tarts. It was always a battle to try and finesse some of the accompanying "hard sauce"—essentially sugar, butter, vanilla extract, and a little flour—out of her without ever actually eating a forkful of the tart. I simply deconstructed it and moved the pieces to strategic positions around the plate in a doomed effort to make it look like I'd eaten some of it.

Sorry, I jumped all the way to Christmas dinner there. We need to get back to the tree.

Once my father had it up—an arduous contest that involved my insistence on helping and getting in the way and prompting a lot of bad language on the part of my father who was attempting to keep the thing upright while at the same time trying to ram it into whatever gimcrack cockamamie tree holder he'd discovered that year—and he was satisfied that its inevitable list to port wasn't going to result in catastrophe, we would begin the process of decoration.

First, the lights. Again, this was my father's purview, as it involved stringing them in such a fashion that the lights of our two ancient strands—manufactured around the time Alexander Graham Bell was demanding, "Watson, come here"—were spaced equally around the tree. My dad was a perfectionist when it came to the lights, getting the right spacing between the different colours, and this sometimes took hours. It wasn't helped that in those days when one bulb didn't work, the entire string didn't work, so it involved much cursing and unscrewing and re-screwing until he found the dead one and then multiple trips to the hardware store—"Jim, these are outdoor lights you got, not indoor lights!"—to get new ones of the appropriate colour. Once they were strung and functioning, my father would step back to admire his handiwork and my mother and I would move in with the ornaments.

I knew the baubles the way I knew my own toys. I'd stared at them on the tree for days and days over many Christmases and they were old friends. There were a few valuable family ones—we managed to break one a year on average—but most were cheap silver, gold, red, and green globes. There were a couple of decorations I'd made in kindergarten and the early grades of school—projects involving paper plates and various cut-out shapes slapped on with the ubiquitous school paste and looking like something a demented blind hermit might produce in his idle hours—and they were accorded pride of place, deep within the boughs where gaps needed camouflaging and where decent folk couldn't see them.

We placed the star on the top and finally, it was time for the tinsel.

Anyone under the age of fifty won't know what I'm talking about when I say tinsel, but believe me, there was a time when tinsel icicles were things of deep glittering beauty. They made the tree. When you see a Christmas tree in an old black and white film, it looks terrific because of the tinsel.

It was lead tinsel.

Lead foil was a popular material for tinsel manufacture until the US Food and Drug Administration declared it to be a risk to children. And it was a risk, if you ate three or four boxes of them, same as if you ate a package of mothballs or drank a quart of gasoline. So North America turned to thin strips of polyvinyl chloride coated with paint which, if a child ate three or four boxes of them, would be toxic, too. Christmas—it seems—is just a really dangerous time to be a child.

Anyway, we used and reused our lead tinsel until it was too tatty to hang and we were forced to chuck it out. For one year, we tried the PVC plastic stuff, but it didn't hang properly, it didn't look right, and if someone walked across the hallway twenty feet from the tree, the plastic tinsel would billow up as if struck by a gale. So we stopped using it. Everyone did.

Anyway, that was our tree. I expect it was pretty much like yours, give or take a few popcorn strands, working lights, and your family's selection of swear words.

In the days leading up to Christmas, my raptor's eyes would be levelled on the mailman coming down the drive, looking for packages arriving from the West. These were nearly always mundane or downright-awful presents—clothes too big or too small for a boy they'd never seen and had known only as the output of their wayward sister and aunt. The worst—and perversely the one I looked forward to—was from a relative-by-marriage of my mother named Aunt Armeral and her two kids, Ched and Ginny.

My mother was no help with their names. She'd just shake her head with a look that said there was no accounting for the tastes of her much older deceased brother. Aunt Armeral and cousins Ched and Ginny lived in rural Saskatchewan. I always pictured Aunt Armeral as a kind of fortune teller, crooning over chicken bones and settling down in front of a roaring fire and bubbling cauldron with a plentiful supply of rash-inducing musk ox wool within easy reach, to knit the thickest socks possible—each at least three inches thick as measured by my ruler—for a nephew apparently suffering from—to judge by the socks' shapelessness—two club feet. In a final happy touch, her knitted gifts were adorned with vague Sign-of-the-Beast patterns above the ankle.

These socks were always a wonder to my family—they made great nests for injured muskrats and birds, being warm and raw and with a design that helpfully warded off evil spirits—but for me, the amazement always stemmed from their names. Ginny was fine but where did the name Armeral come from? And who would willingly name their son Ched? Was it short for Cheddar? If so, why wasn't Ginny named Brie, or Muenster, or Stilton? I never did get an answer to any of these vital questions, as I never met or spoke with them, although many years later I was in a diplomatic receiving line for the British prime minister and his entourage and found myself shaking the hand of a man in the dark suit of a mandarin who introduced himself as "Ched."

Ched? I shook his hand enthusiastically and asked him what Ched was short for.

"Chedwyn."

You would have thought I'd just discovered a long-lost family member, I was so pleased. I gushed at him like a broken water main, babbling and cracking jokes and continuing to pump his arm as he—with increasing desperation—tried to break free. He eventually managed to do so, but only because his wild eye movements were attracting the interest of the prime minister's security team.

The presents from my mother's western relatives went under the tree, to be examined and scrutinized by my expert fingers. From year to year an actual toy or useful device would slip through the family cracks and come to me as a present—a small plastic pinball machine, a little knife in a little sheath—but usually it was clothes for the perpetual four-year-old girl they assumed my mother had birthed and placed in a time stasis bubble. Still, they were presents and they were under the tree and they had my name misspelled in interesting ways on their cards and that spun up the excitement and kept it humming until Christmas Eve.

Christmas Eve in our house was old-time, staid, and the same year after year. I never found it boring, not even in my slump-down-in-the-car-to-avoid-being-seen-with-my-parents teen years.

We would read aloud.

When I was very young, it was just *A Visit from St. Nicholas*, by Clement C. Moore, illustrations by Everett Shinn. You can't beat *The Night Before Christmas*, as it's called today, and Shinn's paintings made the house—with its sleeping mice in matchboxes—as cozy as Christmas should be. My father gradually added Dickens and others and one year, my own short Christmas story that was published in the newspaper's

Teen Talk page. Even at the time, I knew its inclusion in our Christmas Eve readings was something of a sop to a family member, yet the confidence it engendered in me—to be placed in the family's holy pantheon of Christmas Eve writers—was incalculable.

We'd hang our stockings over the fireplace, my mother would put out the glass of milk and the oatmeal cookie, and we would retire.

I never slept well when I was small. I'd be too intent on listening for sounds on the roof above my head. One year, my mother brought a hamster in a cage upstairs—the hamster's name was Ollie and he was a Christmas present for my dad— to keep it out of his sight and earshot. Ollie seized upon the change of scenery to get on his little squeaky wheel and run all night long, so thanks for that, mother.

In our house, a child didn't tumble down to Christmas morning upon awakening. The child was summoned. By a Christmas carol.

When my dad dropped the tone arm of the phonograph in the cabinet hi-fi on the Christmas carols LP—usually "Joy to the World" or "Hark the Herald Angels Sing"—it was the starter's pistol to belt down the stairs—decently attired in pyjamas, dressing gown, and slippers—to see what Santa had brought. This seemed as normal as anything in our house, and so I never gave it any thought that it might just be a way for my parents not to have to deal with a crazed kid at 5 AM and instead, they could yawn, stretch, and put on the coffee before a 7 AM onslaught.

I had no clock or watch in those early years, so I never knew what time it was. There were a couple of years when I'd arise in the dark—thinking it must be about time for the carol—and put on my dressing gown and slippers and lie down on my bed for four or five hours, vibrating.

It didn't matter to me. It was worth it.

Another possible oddity of our house was that Santa's presents weren't distributed under the tree. Instead, they were arrayed along the length of the bench in front of the picture window, and all of them were unwrapped.

Again, fine with me. I could enter the living room and see at a glance what was what, able to quickly home in on the good stuff and leave the new hockey stick or the little plastic bowling set until the end.

When I was older, the presents seemed to subtly change, and by subtly change, I mean Santa seemed to veer away from department store purchases in favour of pickups from used furniture stores or the freebie bin at the newspaper.

Take, for instance, the year I received a "portable" record player. It was visibly old and worn and weighed about the same as a pallet of iron ingots. It looked like the kind of thing that had sat in the room of a senior in a care home and, when its owner went off to her celestial reward, had been recycled back into the general population. It was serviceable though, and if I ever suffered a brain injury, it could play my grandfather's 78 rpm records, but it did seem a little unusual for a fifteen-year-old's Christmas present. My father—sorry, Santa—was obviously aware of this situation, so he placed a brand new record—still in its shrink wrap—right next to it as a kind of offset to the age of the phonograph.

The record was the then-newly released LP by The Rolling Stones—*Their Satanic Majesties Request.* You may remember it as the Stones' response to Sgt. Pepper, with its white-smoke-on-blue-background cover and large 2D-style thick photo glued to it so you could see the band members decked out in psychedelic clothing and silly Hogwarts-type hats sitting cross-legged in front of a mysterious tower under a red Saturn and an oversized moon. It's conceded to be the worst recording of the band's career.

I knew instantly that the record most likely arrived at the newspaper for review purposes, and that my father had picked it out of the freebie bin as his hepcat camouflage for the Edison-era record player. It was for certain that he'd never heard such cuts as "She's a Rainbow" or "Citadel" or "2000 Light Years from Home," although he definitely would later, when I'd play them at volume upstairs, and he'd throw down his book from his reading chair and come to the foot of the stairs and yell, "Turn down that racket!" and then caucus with my mother to discuss the sorry state of contemporary music.

My father's tastes in music ran to Mantovani or *Living Strings Play Music In The Night* at dinnertime, and the occasional marching band number on Sunday mornings when he wanted to feel all martial and military while revelling in—or possibly lamenting—the knowledge that he'd never again have to march to these tunes on a baking drill ground or parade formation.

Some great gifts were laid out on that Christmas bench over the years. A microscope. One of the first small Aiwa tape recorders. A chemistry set.

The latter was initially exciting but ultimately a disappointment. It looked great—a colourful metal box that opened like a book—and had lots of spiffy chemicals in jars and test tubes and stoppers and measuring implements and an alcohol burner, but it quickly became clear that 99 percent of the experiments involved mixing things to produce a different coloured thing. Nothing that went bang. Nothing to create a lingering cloud of death, although burnt sulphur was always a go-to smell for ambitious little chemists and young men of science. Really, the only thing worth doing wasn't even set out in the kit's recommended experiments. What you did was light the alcohol burner, pour a little alcohol into a test tube, and heat it. The alcohol would bubble up inside the test tube until it reached the top whereupon it would burst into a small blue flame, but even creating a small blue flame paled with constant repetition.

The best gifts were always the books. When I was young it was the Rupert Bear series and *Chums* annuals and Boys' Own Adventures and Dale of the Mounted series and the Chip Hilton sports books. When I was older, it was Antoine de Saint-Exupéry's *Wind, Sand and Stars* and *Night Flight* and hilarious collections of S.J. Perelman and P.G. Wodehouse and Canadian humourist Eric Nicol. There was no such thing as a book that was a bad Christmas present. Ever.

Easily the most surprising gift—and certainly the most expensive—was a present for the entire family that my mother set up with a brilliant parental fake-out-the-kid manoeuvre.

I was fourteen when my mother came to me early in December and in a conspiratorial voice told me she had purchased a lawn mower for my father as a Christmas present and that she had the deliveryman put it in our little cabin and locked the door with a padlock.

I should have been suspicious. Why on earth would my mother, who's relationship to yard machinery was on a par with Superman's relationship with green kryptonite, buy my father a lawn mower? Why wouldn't my dad just buy it himself, and why on earth would it be worthy of being a Christmas present? And wouldn't my dad be suspicious about a lock on the cabin door?

But she rightly judged that I had no interest in anything to do with a lawn mower. The story's real purpose was to throw me off the scent of the idea that something interesting might be hidden in the cabin, so job done.

Anyway, we'd finished the presents, and then the stockings— which always held a few candies and chocolates and an orange, and in my mother's stocking, a clanking handful of that particular year's silver dollars—when my mother handed me a padlock key and whispered for me to go open the cabin and bring in the lawn mower.

I took the key, went outside in my slippers, unlocked the door, and inside was a Skidoo.

Snowmobiles had been around for a few years by then and were already starting to feature smart and glossy painted bodies and big engines. This one was a used first-gen Skidoo, with a kind of upright cowling and small exposed engine that threw off fumes in your face, but it was terrific because nobody else in our neighbourhood had one yet and because—after I did the kid math on it—I realized it was basically mine.

The kid math said my mother wouldn't drive it—so that removed a third of its potential possession time—and my dad would only use it for a couple of hours on weekends, meaning it would be mine for the rest of the hours of the week. Kid math.

I had a great time with it. It was slow by comparison with any other snowmobile, but it had one enormous advantage in that it was lightweight. Unlike other machines of the period— before the advent of reverse gears—I could easily pick it up by its rear end and turn it around, meaning that unlike other snowmobiles, I was never stuck. Yeah, I put it through some thin ice a couple of times, and it broke down on me due to a frozen gas line and a clogged carburetor, but I could always manhandle it to a safe place or off to the side of a road. It allowed me to pick up movie or dance dates in what I imagined to be great style— although now that I think about it, none of those first dates led to a follow-up and I'm not sure whether that can be chalked up to the snowmobile or me. Indeed, as I look back, a teenage girl probably did not want to show up for a Friday night at the Shang looking like a member of the Shackleton expedition, or discover upon arrival at the school winter dance that the Yardley Oh! de London she'd carefully dabbed behind the ear and on the neck and on the wrist had somehow turned into a dousing of Eau de Shell 30-weight.

Still, it was fun, and for a year or two, Paul and I went everywhere in winter on that machine. This was before they became cheap and popular and essentially ruined the winter lake in a cacophony of noise and speed.

But back to Christmas Day, where the afternoon was generally spent playing with Paul, comparing presents, listening to new music, or playing with new devices.

Dinner was the turkey set piece—we'd pull the crackers and wear the tissue paper hats—followed by an hour or two of post-turkey stupor, staring at the tree. Bedtime was preceded by the cracking of a new book and the feeling that a great day was passing.

The next day was Boxing Day and that meant piling into the car with my parents and driving south to a town north of Toronto where my dad's parents lived and where we'd open more presents and have a Christmas-style lunch with my dad's family.

Granddad and Nana were always old. So was their house, with a clock that ticked loudly and slowly. They moved slowly and deliberately themselves but were genial and tolerant of me. Granddad played Santa, calling out the names on the presents I handed him from under the magnificent tree with all its Victorian decorations, and his children and grandchildren would come up to receive them from him. We all watched as one by one the presents were opened, remarked upon, and put down. Uncle Tom—my dad's unmarried brother who lived with my grandparents—always gave fabulous gifts, genuine boy stuff. Battery-powered games, water-powered rocket launchers, really excellent swag. My spinster aunt Dora, who also lived with them, always gave something elegant and tasteful and—until I reached my late teens—exceedingly useless. Really, a flower vase? An antique silver calling-card case?

My present from my grandparents never changed. It was always a Viyella shirt.

My grandfather had worked for a shirt manufacturer and Viyella shirts were seen to be the *ne plus ultra* of menswear. He himself wore little else. I received thirteen or fourteen of them over the years but never wore one once. It was a great shirt, no doubt, but it was a mix of cotton and wool and I couldn't wear it without breaking out in a full-torso crimson rash. Nobody ever had the heart to tell Granddad. It would break his heart. But the Salvation Army in Mariposa always benefited from his munificence come January when my mother made her dump-the-unused-presents run. The contribution of the Viyella shirt balanced out all the homemade socks from her side of the family.

Taught me a lesson, though. If you're a granddad, don't give your grandson the thing you love and expect him to love it, too. It'll only end in tears. Which is why I've told my wife that if she ever finds me saying to a grown grandson—"I think you'll love the Electric Prunes' version of '(I Had) Too Much To Dream Last Night.' It's a classic. Let me put it on for you!"—she has my permission to shoot me.

Lunch was a giant baked ham, scalloped potatoes, and four or five jellied salads—one of which would contain grapes and cherries and little coloured marshmallows—and a tomato aspic. My granddad, as founder of the feast, stood at the head of the table. He'd turn off his hearing aid, seize his enormous electric carving knife, and proceed to noisily demolish the ham in showers of shaved pork. He'd lay a two-pound slab on a plate, and all the women would say "Oh dad, that's too much!" but as he couldn't hear he'd nod and dish out a three-pound slab on the next plate.

They're all gone now. I miss them.

But in one sense, I have them still. I have their traditions and their practices. They've found their way to my table and my house and my family and my Christmas tree. Not always complete or intact, but still visible to an eye that can see back a generation and the links between what was and what is.

When I first moved to Vancouver as a young single reporter, I shared an apartment and then a house with friends. We instituted a waifs-and-strays policy for Christmas. We'd put up a Christmas tree and decorate it with tacky baubles from the drugstore sales bin and I'd cook a turkey and the single reporters—and the friends of single reporters—would show up with bottles of wine and unwanted bottles of liqueur and we'd have a great Christmas dinner.

I should probably mention that after my parents moved to Cape Breton, I came back to the *Mariposa Daily Packet & Times* after university for a brief stint as a reporter before moving west. It was in Mariposa where I learned to cook. Or rather, where I learned that I *wanted* to cook.

My roommate in Mariposa was Jack Chen, a great guy whose mother had smuggled him out of China. He'd gone to a US university, learned to become an outstanding photographer—the kind who, when he has nothing to do for thirty seconds, takes his camera apart and puts it back together, just for fun—and came to Mariposa to learn to be a reporter as well as a shooter. I'd help him out when I could, and he helped me out by teaching me why I didn't want to be an editor.

"Can you look at this copy, please?" Jack said.

Sure. Hmmm, you need to add an *s* to the word umbrella here. There are six umbrellas, which makes umbrella a plural—umbrellas—so you need to add the *s* to umbrella.

"But that isn't logical," Jack said. "The word 'six' tells you there's more than one umbrella, so why would you need an *s* when you already know there are six of them?"

Shut up, Jack. You're right. Six tells you there's more than one. You still have to add the *s*, okay? It's the English language. It's not logical. You don't have to understand it. You just have to write it.

And that's why I'll never make a good editor.

Anyway, one day Jack came into the kitchen with some chicken thighs, soaked them in garlic and soy sauce, and steamed them in a wooden steamer. They looked pale but they tasted great. Maybe, I thought, I should learn to cook.

I tried out a pot roast, with mashed potatoes and peas. A young female reporter dropped by and I asked her to stay to dinner. She ate the pot roast and asked me out on a date.

The sound of the scales falling from my eyes could be heard blocks away as one of life's great truths stood revealed.

If you can cook, women will come to your place.

Years later in Vancouver, I served a young woman in a red dress and a Panama hat an appetizer of Crab Louie, followed by a course of rack of lamb, fiddleheads, ratatouille, and tiny nugget potatoes sautéed in butter. She ate the food, bought me a basset hound puppy—the equivalent of a tester kit for a potential husband—and in due course we were married and went to live in an enchanted little house near the water, where I still cook for her.

Anyway, I've learned to put together a crackerjack Christmas dinner, and per my mother, gravy is the key. Weeks before Christmas, I buy a small turkey and simmer it and reduce the broth to a demi-glace, just so I can give serious depth to the Christmas gravy. We have waifs and strays sometimes for Christmas dinner, but it's my kids whose compliments I live for and live off, and they too are cooking turkeys on their own and that's how traditions are passed on.

When they were young and still at home, they couldn't come out of their room Christmas morning until they heard the "Hallelujah" chorus from Handel's *Messiah* on the stereo. Their children in turn will one day be summoned to the tree by music, too.

Some of our tree decorations are from earlier generations, but our kid's artwork is still stuffed inside the boughs where god-fearing people can't see them. And still no tinsel.

There are new family practices threatening to become Christmas tradition.

My daughter and I visit the Reifel Bird Sanctuary—you drive out and across a one-lane wooden bridge to Westham Island near our home—on the afternoon of Christmas Day. We're life members of the Reifel—our names are inscribed on the outer wall of the warming shed, a recognition I cherish above most others—and we carry small bags of oiled black sunflower seeds with us. On Christmas Day, the sanctuary is filled with Asian-Canadian families who seem to be unoccupied with the day's North American traditions.

My daughter and I walk past the milling and cackling ducks to a tree-and-bush-lined trail and get set up. We take a handful of seed in our hand, open the palm so the hand is flat and the seeds are in the middle, and hold them out in front of us. Chickadees descend from the conifers and alight on the branches of the lower bushes. One by one—and then in twos and threes—the chickadees flutter off the bushes and land on our fingers—they weigh about as much as a cotton ball and have little claws that tickle—and they pluck out a seed from the pile and fly off, returning about ninety seconds later for more.

Extended Asian families approach and watch us feeding the birds. We wave them over, pour seed into the hands of their kids, show them how to do it, and smile at their delight when the chickadees come to their hands. Pretty soon there's a line of kids and parents and grandparents, all with their hands out feeding the chickadees from the bags of seed that we've brought along with us. Everyone—and I mean everyone—is smiling.

But here's what the smiling birdfeeders don't know.

When my father died, he was cremated. He wanted his ashes dumped in front of their house in Cape Breton on the Bras d'Or. It's cold and deep dark ocean water but it's where he wanted his component molecules placed. I think his wartime navy days—when he would take convoys of ships across the North Atlantic and never knew if tomorrow would bring death or safety, deprivation or a fresh piece of fruit; where he experienced total fear and total exhaustion, and never knew why he survived while so many friends and acquaintances perished—animated his life, so that when life was over, he wanted to return himself to those waters.

He died in Vancouver—he knew he was dying and had just resettled my mother to be near her grandchildren—so my mother and I flew to Cape Breton. In a friend's boat we toasted his memory with shot glasses of single malt, hucked the glasses out over the water, and then as my mother stepped back—she couldn't watch—I slowly poured my father into the ocean.

The ashes and tiny bone fragments sank in a narrow column through the dark green water for about five feet, and then something happened.

There must have been a halocline, or some sort of temperature gradient, or quirk of the current, because the ashes billowed up. They formed a large white spreading starburst of form and motion just below the surface.

You're always going to remember pouring out your father's ashes, but this was one of the most startling moments of my life. I can see it as clearly as if it were lasered into my brain, along with the look of the water, the sound of the wheeling gulls, the iodine smell of Atlantic seaweed, the texture of the moment.

I did not pour out all his ashes. I saved some and brought them home and kept them on a bookcase for five years until my mother died.

I mixed my dad's ashes with an equal portion of my mother's.

On a cold clear March morning, I made my way to the Reifel Bird Sanctuary and to a spot on a trail that both my parents loved.

On one side is a slough where ducks waddle up the embankment to be fed, and where owls sometimes sleep in the tree branches high above. On the other side are bushes and a salt-water marsh, part of the Strait of Georgia. In the distance are islands and ocean-going ships and snow-capped mountains. Bald eagles soar overhead and in the rushes are blue herons and hummingbirds. Otters and muskrats and a beaver use this little strip of trail to cross back and forth between the fresh water of the slough and the salt water of the marsh, and you can see their footprints in the mud. It is here that I scattered their combined ashes, amid the scenery and the wildlife they adored.

They are buried treasure now. I need no map to find them.

Just around the corner, where the chickadees are waiting, I spread the rest of my mother's ashes.

She loved chickadees. She loved their little sounds and insouciant mannerisms and said it was impossible to be sad or blue or anything but joyful in their presence. Even in her last year, she'd stand in this place, one hand on her cane and one hand raised and open. The chickadees would flutter to her palm, and she'd smile, and the years would fall away, and she was young again.

So on Christmas Day, my daughter and I come to this place and we find the chickadees are waiting for us, perched on the branches of the bushes and the trees that host the atoms of my mother. We hold out our open hands. The birds fly to us.

It doesn't matter if a Christmas tradition is old and used or new and gleaming, what matters—what makes it a glory—is that it lifts the heart.

The Secret Garden

THE HOUSE NEXT to our house was the Richardsons', or at least it was where the Richardson house used to be. Mr. Richardson had spared no expense to build an immaculate red-brick rancher with a back lawn that descended in manicured stages to a concrete seawall.

The Richardsons were retired when they built the house and they built it to last. Everything was high quality, high density, and the glass—from louvred windows to picture window—was custom crafted. I can remember being very small and messing around the foundations as it was built, so it's odd to find that the Richardson house is gone now, torn down—presumably using jackhammers—and replaced by a remarkably charmless two-storey house. The only good news is that the little boathouse Mr. Richardson built is still perched down on the seawall. It too had been constructed out of brick and concrete and built to endure. Mr. Richardson had installed a marine railway and, one summer's day, a trim twenty-four-foot Owens cabin cruiser idled up to the railway crib and was pulled up into the boathouse.

One week later, Mr. Richardson let the cruiser down the slipway into the water and assisted Mrs. Richardson aboard from the dock. They took the cruiser for a little spin up and down the waterfront before returning it to its cradle, pulling it up into the boathouse, and never venturing out in it again. Boating wasn't the Richardsons' thing, but their boathouse was a wonder to a kid who could squeeze under its retractable door. The inside was spotless, like an operating theatre. There were new fishing poles and paddles and life jackets hung perfectly along its painted walls, unsullied by human hands, the cabin cruiser pristine and dry as a cactus carving. When I left for university, the boathouse still smelled new.

If the Richardson house being torn down was disconcerting, it was nothing compared with the next two houses on the waterfront. Both are contemporary, well kept, and completely foreign to me. It requires a concentrated act of memory to wipe away these houses and their manicured lawns and summon up the single shaggy property that used to occupy this section of the street.

It belonged to someone called Ferguson. I never met him, her, or them, and never saw anyone connected with the place, but to the neighbourhood it was always Fergusons'.

The public view of the Ferguson property used to be a tall green wooden fence that blocked the view from Bay Street as well as from the North Street extension that ran to the water's edge and bounded it on its south side. These views were further masked by overhanging maple and elm boughs. The north side of the property was hidden behind a twenty-foot-high hedge shared with the Richardson property.

The only break in the fenced façade was an old wooden garage with peeling white paint that was set into the fence along Bay Street, its garage door padlocked. There were no gates or entrances to the property of any kind.

There didn't need to be. There was no house. There hadn't been since Hurricane Hazel blew through Mariposa in 1954.

Mariposa isn't usually subject to hurricanes, but Hazel was an unusual storm. It killed more than a thousand people as it rampaged through the West Indies and up the east coast of the United States, where it faltered until it merged with a cold front over Pennsylvania. It regained hurricane status and headed north, eventually stalling over Toronto and killing another eighty people, mostly through flooding. Old-timers remember it rained for seven days before Hazel arrived, so that when the hurricane showed up and stalled, every stream and river in southern Ontario overflowed.

The irony is that on the night Hurricane Hazel and its winds and torrential rains arrived in Mariposa, the Ferguson house burned down. It burned to the ground in the middle of a hurricane and nobody noticed. The Fergusons, whoever they were, had the debris cleaned out but left the foundations as they were. The impenetrable high green wall was put up around the property and the garage and it sat there, its trees and gardens and grasses untended and untouched for the next sixteen years.

It was like growing up one door down from The Secret Garden.

Paul and I early on accessed the property from the lake and, using an old willow on the shore to hang a rope swing, we'd climb up and swing out and cannonball into deep water. Exploring the property, we found a loose board in the fence off Bay Street that we could manipulate like a door to get in and out, eliminating the need for a water approach. We made forts, dug holes for no particular reason, lay on our backs in the deep grass, and watched the birds in the trees above. In summer we'd bring home bouquets of irises and peonies to our mothers from its ghostly gardens, baskets of plums and apples in early autumn.

I used to take books and magazines and a sandwich in waxed paper and curl up by myself in a spot under an old maple near the water embankment and read and while away the hours.

These were still the summer days when a kid went out the screen door in the morning and didn't return until dinner. The day was yours to do with as you pleased, to roam or stay put, to play sports or read, to explore or to lie in a hammock, to bicycle or play on the swings in the park or look in all the store windows along Main Street, to explore the lumberyard or see what was being built in the boatyard. You used to be able to do it unsupervised in your city and in your town, and it's something that has disappeared from the former if not entirely from the latter.

We've no doubt gained something through increased supervision of the young—skills from lessons, abilities from supervised activities—but something's been lost, too. I think it's the opportunity to be free to discover what it is you like to do rather than be told what you should do and how to do it.

I don't know if I learned anything from the summer hours in the Ferguson lot—certainly it was nothing concrete or quantifiable—but I do know that it provided the genesis of a unique friendship in my life, one that will survive as long as my river runs and led to one of the best Christmas gifts I'll ever receive.

It began one summer day as I was napping in the tall grass near the overgrown garden by the south fence of the Ferguson lot, a library book on dinosaurs in my hand.

A shadow fell over my face. I opened my eyes to find a short Indigenous woman standing over me. I couldn't have been more surprised if it had been a Martian. I'd never seen anyone but Paul inside the Ferguson perimeter fence, and an Indigenous woman was really pushing the startle button. I remained flat on the ground.

She smiled, tapped the dinosaur book with her foot, and said, "Library?"

I nodded.

She turned and said something to someone. I used the opportunity to stand, and a boy—my height, my size, my age—appeared next to her.

"This is Ray," the woman said. "He's staying with me from Alberta. He has need of the library. Would you be able to take him there?"

I nodded again, said "Sure," and added, "Um, now?"

"Yes, thank you. I'll wait here."

She had a waterproof bag with her, and she opened it. Inside was a penknife, a small set of shears, and a tiny hand scythe made out of wood. She took out the scythe and slowly began to work its edge against the base of the tall grass that grew outside the shade of the maple, cutting it neatly and making a careful pile.

"You can't cut this grass with a metal edge," she said. "It would be disrespectful."

I didn't know what to say, so I asked Ray if he had a bike. He shook his head.

"Wanna ride double with me?" I asked.

He nodded his head.

I took Ray through the fence and we went to my place to collect my bicycle. He eased onto the seat and I rode him double down to the Mariposa library. I jabbered most of the way there. Ray kept his answers to single words.

We arrived at the library and I took him downstairs to the kids' section. I looked to see if any new dinosaur or astronomy books had been added. Ray, after a cursory look, wandered off into the adult sections.

After ten minutes, I was ready to go with a picture book on the planets. Ray was ready too, holding a book on internal combustion engine maintenance, an engineering textbook, and a book on the history of the Nobel Prize. I checked them all out on my library card.

On the ride back to Fergusons', Ray turned talkative. The old woman was his aunt who he was visiting for the summer. He was Blackfoot, his aunt was Ojibwe. He explained that neither his uncle nor his aunt had a library card and he wanted to know how to fix his uncle's car. Oh, and he'd set himself a goal to learn engineering over the summer.

I had no reply to that. I thought engineering was what you did on trains.

Once back at Fergusons', we found his aunt waiting with a gift for each of us. She'd made two small bracelets, weaving the grass together into three coils and then braiding the coils together into a tight little rope, tied with a knot.

"This is sweetgrass," she told us. "You wear it for good luck."

She said she and Ray would return at the same time in one week with the library books, weather permitting. She took Ray's books and put them in the watertight bag, and they went down to the shore where a canoe had been hauled up on the bank. Ray got in and sat in the bow seat. His aunt pushed off and sat in the stern. They paddled straight out from shore, heading for the middle of the lake.

I went home and twenty minutes later I looked out over the lake. The canoe was a distant dot. They were paddling toward Jikana, the Ojibwe reserve on the far side of Chief Island.

Next week, I went back to Fergusons' and there was Ray and his aunt. Once again, Ray and I biked to the library, where he took out more incomprehensible books, and the two of them paddled back across the lake.

Over the summer, Raymond Big Cloud and I became loose friends, comfortable in one another's company but with no desire to do much more or to expose one another to other boys.

One day in August, Ray's aunt—her name was Ruth Snache— declared she was going to walk downtown and we could either come along or hang around Fergusons'. I asked if it was okay to take Ray out in our little sailing pram. Ruth said that was fine and left us to our own devices.

Our sailing pram—named *Poliwog*—was a little seven-foot dingy fitted with a mast, a centreboard that could be dropped into a raised slot amidships, and a rudder that fit on the stern. My father had purchased it allegedly so I could learn to sail, but really it was a stopgap until he could get himself a real sailboat.

I brought Ray to our house, rigged the pram, hoisted the sail, and we set off, working upwind so as to come home with the wind at our backs.

Ray, who had never sailed, watched how I handled the boat, and when we switched positions in the cramped dingy he took over as if he'd been sailing all his life.

My father was home for lunch and watched us from the porch. I had made a point of not mentioning Ray or his aunt to my parents, but they didn't seem surprised to see me show up out of the blue with an Indigenous boy to go sailing. My mother made us sandwiches and my father complimented Ray on his seamanship.

I saw Ray and Ruth one more time that summer. The next summer, they didn't show up. Or the summer after that. I assumed Ray had stopped coming east from Alberta and I more or less forgot about him.

I was in my thirties—married and writing a political column for the *Vancouver Sun*—and walking though the Ottawa airport when I felt a tap on my shoulder.

Startled, I turned. In front of me stood a handsome six-foot-six Indigenous man in black clothes, cowboy boots, and black hair in a braid down his back.

It took me a few seconds.

"Ray?"

It was.

We had a Glenlivet in the bar and caught up. We discovered we shared mutual interests such as The Clash and Jim Harrison novellas, but it was clear Ray's intellect resided many floors above my own.

Ray had entered the University of Alberta at a ridiculously early age on full scholarship and blazed through postgraduate work at the University of Toronto, his doctoral thesis in molecular biology an instant classic at age nineteen. He declined a flood of teaching and research positions in favour of a post at the National Research Council in Ottawa that allowed him to work on his own projects at his own speed.

I moved to Ottawa and for five years we would get together every few months, usually at my place where he'd sometimes bring a date, always a beautiful woman. Good-looking women seemed mad for him, yet as my wife noted, he was unfailingly polite and aloof with them.

Being a world-class scientist, and Indigenous to boot, he was awash in requests to speak at institutional gatherings and scientific conferences, and the CBC was desperate to have him on camera whenever it could. *MacLean's* described him—incredibly—as "typical of a savvy new breed of academic warrior who is bringing recognition to Canada's aboriginal population."

"Yeah, well, I had a few reservations about that article," he said, laughing.

In general, Ray shunned the spotlight and celebrity and the gorgeous women who frisked around him like kittens. So it came as something of a surprise when he showed up for dinner one night with a short Asian woman with a soft voice and coke-bottle glasses and the name of Lily and introduced her as his fiancée. Ray was solicitous and almost puppyish with her. Their affection for one another was obvious. She, too, was a research scientist. Three months later, they moved to Calgary where two universities and a research institute were setting up a lab for them.

I was moving, too—back to Vancouver—and had sent my family ahead and was planning to join them the day before Christmas when I got a call from Ray, asking me to stop in Calgary on the way home.

"I know you're a Christmas guy but I think you might want to be here Christmas Eve," he said. "I'm going out with my uncle to a special place and I wanted to see if you could join us. I can get you on an early flight out of here that'll get you home in time to open presents and have your Christmas breakfast with the family."

Ray had spent a couple of Christmases with us in Ottawa and knew how seriously I took Christmas. If he was inviting me to meet his uncle on Christmas Eve, it must be for a reason. I was intrigued. I said I'd be there.

I flew out of Ottawa late in the afternoon on the day before Christmas with a bottle of eighteen-year-old Bunnahabhain and Ray met me at the Calgary airport. "Here," I said, handing him the bottle. "It's old enough to drive, vote, marry, and go to war. Where are we going?"

"You'll see," he said. "We've got a bit of a drive to pick up my uncle tonight but we'll be back in plenty of time for your 5 AM flight."

Outside, we got in his SUV and he tossed me a pair of mukluks and a parka. "We'll be outside tonight. You'll need these."

I asked where in the hell we were going.

"We're going to a place near Bassano, about 140 klicks east of here. We'll pick up my uncle at a spot on the way. When we get there, we'll have to walk a bit, so that's why the mukluks. It'll be cold. Should be a clear night, though."

And why will we be walking around in the cold and the dark?

"You'll see when we get there. Think of it as repayment."

Repayment?

"Yeah. Remember when we first met in Mariposa? You took me to the library on your bike? Let me use your library card?"

Yes.

"I was a shy kid. A visitor. I didn't know a lot of white people. So it meant a lot to me. You showed me kindness and I wanted to repay that."

I said I didn't know if it was kindness so much as fear of his aunt.

She scared me, showing up out of nowhere that day, I said. She was pretty witchy.

Ray laughed. "Yeah, well, I still believe it was a kind thing to do. And it's my family's witchy-ness that's brought us here tonight. I can't promise anything. Still, if it happens for you, I think you'll find it pretty amazing. And that will please me."

We drove east on the Trans-Canada in the clear moonless dark, talking of this and that. After about ninety minutes, we pulled into a gas station where an old man in a hooded parka was waiting near the pumps.

Ray's uncle didn't say a word as he got in the rear seat. Ray didn't introduce us. We continued driving, then turned down a ploughed side road. We did a little backcountry driving, turning here and there, until Ray pulled the vehicle over by a fence.

"We walk from here," he said, turning off the engine.

We helped his silent uncle over the wire fence and set out across a field toward one of the small rises in the distance. It was easy walking on the snow and frozen ground. The mukluks helped. There was a brisk wind but it didn't bite. Ray let his uncle go ahead, and we followed a short distance behind.

"Are you familiar with the concept of a medicine wheel?" Ray asked me.

I said I'd heard of them but never seen one.

"Well, you won't really see one tonight. The stones are covered by snow. The one we're going to up ahead is the Majorville

Medicine Wheel. It's called Iniskim Umaàpi. If you were to see it in summer, you'd see a pile of stones—a cairn—near the crest of a small hillock. The cairn is surrounded by a stone circle connected by more than two dozen spokes, although you have to mostly imagine the spokes because they're not continuous."

"Weren't the medicine wheels for ceremonial purposes?" I asked. "Or for the buffalo hunt? Or something to do with the equinox?"

"They're thought to be involved with all those things. However, the truth is we really don't know. People have attached all manner of speculation as to their use, both practical and ceremonial. From a scientific standpoint, we don't know what this one's for because it doesn't seem to be good for any of them. It doesn't function as an observatory or a calendar. People have been examining it for years and it doesn't seem to do anything that people imagine it should do. I've had a go at it and I can tell you it doesn't do anything of a practical nature very well, if at all.

"I'll tell you what I do know though," he said.

"It's old. More than 4,500 years old. We know that it has been continuously used as a repository for offerings—sage, sweetgrass, willow leaves, and the like—for all that time. Archaeologists have found evidence of all these offerings in the cairn. It has more than 4,500 years of accreted offerings, layer upon layer of them, and that makes it one of the oldest religious monuments in the world.

"It's not anywhere near as impressive as a pyramid or a Greek temple or a Mayan ruin—I mean, a teenager could dismantle it in an afternoon—yet this splatter of stones has survived the millennia, and while the pharaohs and Mayans have come and gone, people like my uncle continue to come here and use this wheel. My uncle's people don't really understand it, but they continue to use it. More important, they know *how* to use it. There are times they feel that things can happen here, and so they come here to make it happen. Tonight is one of those nights.

"I was here with my uncle more than twenty years ago when something happened," he said. "I'm a trained scientist but I can't tell you what it is. It's something you have to feel. It happens in the part of your brain that resists reason. It's not earth-shattering. In fact, it's really quite a small thing. If it happens and you feel it, though, it can be life-changing."

Ray looked at me.

"My uncle told me tonight would be a good night, and he agreed to let me bring you with me to watch because it would allow me to repay a soul debt. And you've come, so let it unfold. No talk. If it happens, I'm betting you won't want to talk about it."

Okay.

Ahead, Ray's uncle was plodding along and beginning the walk up a mild incline. As we drew closer to the crest of the hillock, we could see a slight hump, presumably the snow-covered cairn. He stopped a short distance away from it and gestured for us to stand off to the side.

In the distance in front of us, the land descended to the frozen Bow River, and beyond was a rising and falling snow-covered prairie landscape faintly illuminated by the bright stars overhead. The wind was stronger here on the crest, but not bitter. I could make out random lumps under the snow but could not get a visual sense of it being a medicine wheel.

We stood like statues in the wind. Nobody spoke. Something was going to happen. I had no idea what it might be, but I did not want to be the one to break the spell.

I became aware that Ray's uncle was muttering something, chanting almost inaudible phrases with his chin on his chest. This continued for some time. Instead of fidgeting as I might usually do, I found myself content to stand still. There was no discomfort. It seemed pleasant and entirely natural to be out on the plain, standing in the cold and the wind under a blanket of brilliant stars.

Then, at some unspoken and unseen signal, Ray's uncle walked a few paces to the cairn, threw back his head, and opened his arms to the sky above and the earth beneath.

Sparks. I swear it.

The stars were like a river of light. It seemed as if he was running his fingers through them, sifting them like diamond sand. You felt there was electricity crackling between him and the wheel and the sky.

I suddenly knew exactly where I was on the planet.

I could feel the earth moving beneath the stars, sense the dormant prairie grass spreading out around me like the sea, hear the wind sweeping in from the mountains at the edge of that sea, and behind it—beyond it—a deeper sound. I tried to focus on that sound but each time I did, it retreated. It was like a distant rumbling, a far-off pounding of something large and immense, something on the move.

And then, as suddenly as it came, it was over.

Ray's uncle lowered his arms, turned, and walked over to us. He stopped in front of Ray, reached up and put his hands on Ray's shoulders. Ray bowed until they touched heads.

Ray's uncle came over and stood in front of me, putting his hands on my shoulders. I bowed and we touched heads.

Then he turned and walked down the slope toward the distant car.

"Merry Christmas," Ray said.

I knew Ray did not believe in the stable or the manger or the star. Or the Virgin and her boy child. Or Mohammed. Or that it was the trickster raven that brought light to the world.

He believed in science. In deduction. In reason.

But now I knew he also believed in an old man, a circle of stones, and the distant thunder of matted hooves on frozen plains.

And because of a chance meeting in the sweetgrass of an unsupervised summer day in a secret garden spawned by a rogue hurricane, so did I.

"Merry Christmas," I said, and we walked down the slope toward the car and Christmas Day.

A Choir Will Sing

THE NORTH STREET extension that divides the Bay Street shoreline properties runs right to the water's edge. Time was when people would back their boat trailers down the extension to launch their small craft into the lake. I was curious if it still acted as a boat launch.

It doesn't.

You couldn't launch a boat off a trailer here today unless you first ploughed through a couple of trees and did an Evel Knievel off a five-foot berm into the lake.

It's too bad because I'd seen a lot of interesting little craft launched here over the years, and never more interesting or downright exciting than the day Paul and I were rooting around the rocks for crayfish and a jaunty little sports car came tooling down the North Street extension toward us.

Paul and I were car nuts, but we'd never seen this type before. It was a small high-riding red convertible with a sort of angled front end and narrow tail fins and resembled a dumpy Sunbeam Alpine. The car slowed as it approached the shoreline. The driver—a middle-aged nondescript man—tooted the horn and waved and drove the car into the lake.

It didn't sink. Instead, a small wake churned out of its rear end and it proceeded—with the occasional wet fart pop of an exhaust sound—to motor away on the lake.

Paul and I lost our minds. It was as if a Volkswagen had sprouted wings and taken to the skies. A car that turned into a boat? Could there be anything cooler?

The driver swung his auto boat in a long lazy turn and headed back to the launch site and drove right back up on the road. He stopped.

We couldn't believe it. We deluged him with questions as he used a grease gun on various points around the car.

The vehicle was an Amphicar, manufactured in West Germany, with two large white propellers—tucked under the trunk—driven by a Triumph engine. Its hood ornament actually contained the bow running lights, and there was a spot to screw in a stern pole light that was required, said the owner, by the Coast Guard. It also sported a bilge pump and a water latch in each door to seal them so water wouldn't leak into the interior.

Paul and I were young, but we knew immediately this was not a car so much as a really, really terrific toy.

Which, of course, is what any great sports car is. All you can ask of any sports car is that it drive ten-year-old boys out of their heads with adoration and amazement.

Women, I would come to learn, are surprisingly immune to the charms of sports cars. My wife never truly shared my love for my Austin Healey "Bugeye" Sprite, with its two fold-down half-moon Brooklands windscreens and its practical and moneysaving ability to pass under an airport parking lot's automated exit arm. To her, the Bugeye's value was you could take your fussing firstborn child and plunk her in a basket in the Sprite's passenger seat, and the baby would be asleep in one slow burbling circuit of the neighbourhood.

The Amphicar owner, having so obviously achieved the car's primary intent in driving small boys wild with the coolness of the thing, was able to drive off knowing that an amphibious vehicle was not an expensive play toy. On the contrary, it was a practical purchase worth every dollar or Deutschmark he'd paid to a smiling vendor.

The little cottage that had once squatted on the shore facing the boat launch and the long array of Ferguson fence has since sprouted new and expensive additions, like grafts on an old-growth trunk. In my time it had been a small rental property, favoured by the school board as a temporary landing site for incoming teachers. One of those teachers had been a Hungarian émigré who played a small but necessary role in my academic career and who gave me one of the saddest and most memorable Christmas Eves ever.

His name was Louis Zagar and he was the worst high school teacher who ever was.

It's not that Louis was stupid or uneducated or swung to school on vines. On the contrary, Louis was among the most educated men in town. We knew this because Big Jimmy Rhomes—the father of Steve, a high school friend of mine—had done the background check on him.

Big Jimmy ran the finance company in our town. For those unfamiliar with what "the finance company" means in a town like Mariposa, it means that if for some reason you couldn't borrow money from one of the established banks, you went to see Big Jimmy about your loan. Big Jimmy's job ensured he knew everything about everybody's background.

Big Jimmy—who was five-foot-four—said Louis had been a big shot in his native Hungary. Eminent lawyer, judge, law professor, spoke six languages.

War hero, too. A Hungarian resistance fighter against the Nazis, Louis had met Yugoslavia's Marshal Tito when he was still Josip Broz and had pulled German shrapnel out of his leg. Tito, remembering the Hungarian's kindness, sent Louis a bottle of his personal liqueur and a box of smoked boar meat every year.

Louis lit out of the homeland in 1956 when the Soviet tanks clanked over the cobbles below his Budapest apartment. He emigrated to Canada because he'd met Canadian paratroopers during the war and thought them fine fellows. But when Louis arrived in Canada, they wouldn't let him practise law. There was a temporary ban on hiring foreign academics and lawyers at the time, so Louis decided to take a short-term job to establish his bona fides and answered a call for a high school French teacher in Mariposa.

Everyone knew Louis spoke beautiful French. Listening to him recite a poem in French or declaring that the pen of his aunt was in the garden, was as good as a trip to Paris, postcards and all. Problem was, his English wasn't the best. He spoke six languages but he couldn't wrap his tongue around the King's English without leaving a heavy accent hanging in the air. In a small Anglophone town like ours, that marked him.

A mechanic could speak with an accent, a lawyer couldn't.

The baker could speak with an accent, but not the cop.

Or a teacher.

Only one position in our high school was allowed to be occupied by someone with an accent and that was the post of art teacher, occupied for many years by the overly Italianated Tony Figaro.

Tony's daily command—"Let's-a all-a paint-a!"—was part of the school lexicon. Never mind—unbeknownst to the school board at the time—that Tony Figaro was really Anthony Jones from out on the Sixth Concession who'd come back from the war with the ability to sing two refrains from one Italian opera and able to offer as his work samples some drawings he'd traced from a book on da Vinci. Art teachers were thin on the postwar ground, and when he was interviewed for the job, Tony responded to all questions with, "I am-a learn your language, si?" The hiring committee made him promise there'd be no nudes in the classroom and, after some of the men on the board had taken him aside and secured his promise to appear before a closed-door meeting of the Kinsmen Club to lecture on the Italian nude, the job was his.

The board was pleased at how quickly Tony's English language improved with exposure to the classroom. Why, he was speaking as good as any of us, they said, and after only one year of exposure to Mariposa's school children. That's the power of education for you.

But the old must give way to the new and by the time Louis appeared before the hiring committee, its petrified attitudes were on the way out and a more supple future was waiting to be ushered in. Louis's credentials were impeccable. He was obviously a man of great learning, and if the infernal bureaucrats in Ottawa and Toronto couldn't see their way to accrediting and credentialing a deserving applicant to the bar or the bench, the Mariposa School Board would show them the foolishness of their ways by hiring Louis Zagar as their high school French teacher.

It made them feel good to perform a good deed, hiring an aristocrat down on his luck. "Hell," said the committee chairman, "we're hiring him for his French, not his English."

So Louis Zagar and his accent came to the Mariposa District Collegiate and Vocational Institute. He spent his first few months at the rental cottage on Bay Street—where you'd see him walking up North Street whistling every morning—before taking up proper digs in an upstairs apartment in a two-storey red-brick house on Neywash Street, across from the Presbyterian church.

It became apparent, however, that while Louis knew his conjugating oats, he couldn't get his students to tie on the nosebag. He simply didn't understand his Mariposa students.

Louis had been accustomed to teaching university students in Budapest—students who wanted to learn and had often made great sacrifices to do so. He had never had to teach high school French in a small Ontario town where, despite its status as one of the country's two languages, nobody ever heard French much less felt the need to speak it. He couldn't understand why seemingly bright kids would ignore the opportunity to speak a new and venerable language, choosing instead to fool around in class and play crappy tricks on their teacher.

He was not a disciplinarian. Which meant many of his high school students felt they could get away with jerking him around.

He would try reason with them. A mistake, of course. Nobody reasons with high school students, not in a class they find boring and inconsequential and where the teacher fails to command their attention with a yardstick or something in the blunt instrument line. But because he was a genial soul and lacking the heart to mete out corporal punishment, he was taken advantage of. Unmercifully.

"Do you do this to me?" he'd say to a misbehaving grade eleven student. "You leave me no choice. I sew you out!"

The difference between being "thrown out" and "sewn out" of a class was significant. Telling your parents you'd been thrown out of a class was one thing, but telling them some guy had "sewn" you out? In our little town at that time, wrapped thin as we were in our bolt of societal cloth, parental consequences tended to be mild.

Not for me, though.

I regret to inform you I was one of those smartass grade eleven students, and when I had to explain to my parents my own expulsion-for-a-day from class, I chose to do so in the wry and chuckling manner of someone inviting his kin to share the joke. I was confident they'd see the hopelessness of being instructed by a man who couldn't pronounce the word "throw."

Their reaction—my father's in particular—was unexpected.

Turned out my father was not tolerant of my attitude. Turned out he held strong views on an Ontario kid learning French.

Turned out I had kicked a wasp's nest.

He ordered me to return to Louis's class the next day, apologize for my behaviour, and if there were any reoccurrence of my behaviour, the consequences would be dire.

It seems I had failed to consider the context into which I was feeding my blasé explanation of expulsion.

See, a year or two earlier my father had written a newspaper editorial for the *Mariposa Daily Packet & Times* that struck a chord with readers. The editorial was picked up and reprinted in a number of Canadian newspapers. The Governor General read it aloud in an address to the Press Gallery dinner in Ottawa, and it was printed on placemats in Canada's Expo pavilion.

The editorial was short, and some of the names appear dated today, possibly unfamiliar, and it's written before we had an official flag or anthem, but it sums up my dad—and his reaction to my nonchalant slagging of Louis Zagar—in the paragraph outlining his view on the use of English and French in Canada.

It's called "The Canada I Love: An Unfashionable Testament." Have a read. It's only 404 words.

I love Canada.

MacLean's Magazine assures me that no Canadian loves his country, and a thousand critics inform me that there is no such thing as a Canadian, no separate and distinct identity.

I am one.

Politicians and pundits assure me there is no Canadian flag, no Canadian national anthem, but I am content with our flag, a sort of red ensign with the Canadian coat of arms in the fly, and I am always moved when a good band plays "The Queen," but I could learn to stand up for "O Canada," too.

I love Canada.

There are people like René Levesque and Marcel Chaput who alternately assail me for oppressing my French-Canadian brothers and threaten me with a promise to pull Quebec out of confederation, but I have been shipmates with Johnny Bernatchez and drank with the Van Doos and kissed Ghislaine Gagnon and voted for St. Laurent and saluted George Vanier and cheered Jean Béliveau, and I know they're Canadians, too. We both learn each other's language, and though their English and my French might be a bit shaky in spots, we're none the worse for that.

I love Canada.

The Americans think I'm a Limey and the English think I'm a Yank, but I feel wise and superior in the States and young and vigorous in England, and I wouldn't trade my country for both of them. Oh, I know the Americans have more money and the British have more poise, but I like to think that Canadians combine the best features of both their ways of life.

I love Canada.

Our politics are dull and our sports bush league, but you can't beat the beer or the air. Oh, there are Nathan Cohen and the Argos and Gordon Sinclair and Réal Caouette but you have to take the rough with the smooth, same as anywhere else.

Torontonians think Canada lies south of Muskoka between the Humber and the Bluffs, but I have crossed

the Yukon and trod the lonely beaches of the Queen Char-
lottes, felt the Chinook's warm breath across the prairie
snow, boiled lobster above the Fundy tideline, and picked
blueberries on the bare hills above St. John's. It is a magnificent country, the most richly varied in climate and scene in
all the world, home of a vigorous and warm-hearted people,
a country to be proud of.

I am a Canadian. Are there any more like me?

Although it was unsigned—as all his editorials were—my
father was proud of this one and I expect he'd be damned if
any kid of his would wound the family or nation's honour with
a wanton mocking of an official language or the accent of its
instructor.

I presented myself to Louis the next day and duly apologized.

It was worth it. Louis and I ended up sitting down after
school that day for a little back-and-forth that included his
asking for ideas on how better to teach and manage the class.

I don't know if my answer was lame or inspired, but I
thought it pretty good at the time.

Here's what you do, I said.

Divide the class into boys and girls, ask the girls to go wait
in the hall, and close the door. Show the boys a picture of Brigitte Bardot.

Send the boys out, bring in the girls, and show them a picture of some good-looking French guy.

Then tell everyone, that's why we should learn French.

I can't speak for anyone else, I said, but I sure as hell would
want to be able to talk to Brigitte Bardot.

Louis laughed and said it was an interesting idea.

What he did next was to take the idea and make it better.

A couple of days later, as he was writing on the blackboard
and had his back to us, the front row kids used their feet to

push his desk closer to the blackboard and moved their own desks up. They did this three times, with the result that when Louis turned to face us, his desk was about three feet from the blackboard.

Instead of turning red and yelling, Louis calmly put down his chalk, asked all the girls to step into the hall for a minute. When the last girl had exited, he closed the door, turned on the school's slide projector, walked to the front of the class, and pulled down the white screen above the blackboard. On the screen was projected a picture of Brigitte Bardot.

Those lips. That cleavage. Those eyes. That cleavage.

"I'd like you to imagine you are sitting in your booth at the Golden Shangri-La downtown," he said. "You're having a Coke. You look up to see Brigitte Bardot approaching your booth. She sits down across from you. She looks at you. She leans forward. She takes your hand. She looks into your eyes and she begins talking to you."

We all stared at the screen, imagining it.

"Don't you think you'd like to know what she's saying? Don't you think you'd like to know what she's asking you? Don't you think you'd like to be able to respond to her?

"*Mes amis*, that's why it's worth learning the French language."

He sent the boys out, brought the girls in, and while the boys caucused in the hallway and agreed that the one word we'd all be saying to Brigitte was "*Oui*," he showed them a picture of the young and roguish actor Alain Delon and gave them the same spiel.

For the next few weeks, we all did our French homework and behaved in class. Not because we believed that Brigitte or Alain was going to show up at the Shang any time soon to plead for our company and companionship, but because we were grade eleven students and we harboured the attitude that, "Hey, it *could* happen, right?"

Meanwhile, my father was sensing bilingualism in the air and, wishing me to have a jump on life, determined that four weeks of my summer should be spent in a Quebec City suburb in a French immersion course. My high school French mark was going to be of some importance.

Problem was, I was still a terrible language student. Despite actually doing the assigned homework, my final French mark that year was a 57, three short of the 60 that was the minimum requirement for the Quebec summer school.

Louis, knowing of my summer plans, raised my mark to 61.

Nobody asked him to do it. He just went ahead and did it.

It never occurred to me to thank him. It would have been out of character for me to give thanks and out of character for him to get some.

When I returned from Quebec—able to order Coke and chips anywhere in the francophone world—Louis was ill. It was no secret. It was all around the school that he had cancer. The other teachers seemed to take a perverse delight in announcing that Louis had the Big C, as if our behaviour had been the cause and that we'd better not try and give it to them or there'd be real trouble.

By this time, I was off in private school, but I heard that Louis was away from class for days at a time, and that he was growing thin and pale and nobody was playing tricks on him anymore.

I was back in Mariposa for Thanksgiving break and was walking through Mariposa Beach Park on my way home from the pool hall when I saw him sitting on a bench under a tree near the shore. He was wearing an elegant long blue coat, a white silk scarf round his neck, smoking an enormous pipe. He saw me, and beckoned.

"*Bonjour, Monsieur Zagar,*" I said. "*Comment allez-vous?*"

He said my accent was much improved and asked me how I had enjoyed Quebec City.

I said the courses had been hard.

"No," he said, he did not want to know about the courses. What had I thought of Quebec City, so European compared to Mariposa?

Thanks to Steve's father, I knew all about Louis's love of European cities, so I told him the truth. I told him I'd loved it.

Every spring since he'd arrived in Mariposa, Louis would come to Big Jimmy's office at the finance company and borrow a sum of money against his salary. "I was feeling in a good mood the first time he walked in, and I lent him the dough," Big Jimmy said. "He paid it back promptly. Same thing every year, like clockwork. Whatever he needs, I'll give it to him. He's no risk at all."

What Louis did with the money was surprising.

Each summer, according to Steve's father, Louis would go abroad. He'd return to his native Budapest and rent what Big Jimmy referred to as "a classy set of digs." It was his way of retaining something of his former life, that of a man of culture, entertaining his literary and arts friends with wine and dinner in his summer apartment overlooking the river.

With three weeks left in his summer vacation, he'd travel to Wales and spend his time in a town south of Swansea. Nobody knew why.

So sitting with him on the bench in the park, with Louis talking of the places he loved in Europe—places such as the island of Brioni, where he'd been Tito's guest at the old fox's palatial retreat—and mentioning Wales, I asked him why he went there, as he obviously wasn't Welsh.

For the singing, he said. For their male choirs and their hymns. Having an audience, it was a subject on which he was happy to speak.

He had been on a tour of the British Isles on his first vacation out of Canada—Hungary being too full of hot-and-cold-running communists at the time—and had visited Wales because of his love for rugby. He'd attended an international rugby match at Cardiff Arms Park, and when the red jerseys of Wales ran out onto the pitch, the crowd stood and sang the national anthem, "Land of My Fathers." In Welsh, "Hen Wlad Fy Nhadau."

The sound of that hymn, he said, the passion with which the crowd sang it, the way the wind seemed to carry the melody up out of the stadium and across the hills, moved him beyond words.

He said it reminded him of the songs of his own country, the songs men had sung in his youth, songs and voices that were now silenced. Take the song out of men and you take the spirit out of their hearts, he said.

To keep that spirit alive, Louis returned each year to Wales to hear songs sung by men who might be beaten down but were never beaten. He travelled anywhere there was a good men's choir. To the famous old towns of Rhymney, Tredegar, and Treorchy, and Pontypridd, where the father-and-son team of James and Evan James composed the national anthem and where there was a memorial declaring the Jameses had been "inspired by a deep and tender love of their native land."

Louis said he understood what that meant. Unable to find that feeling in his own homeland at the time, he was delighted and invigorated to find it among the Welsh. There can be no greater religion, he said, no greater cause than to honour such men and such hymns.

I asked him why he hadn't resumed his career in the law. Why stay a French teacher in Mariposa?

He said he'd meant to early on, but that once he'd mastered the knack of teaching high school he felt less and less inclined to return to the law or to the university common room.

"I like the town here," he said, "I like the people. A little parochial, yes, but good people. I had my summers away. It was enough."

That night I told my father what Louis had said about Wales and songs and men's choirs.

I returned to boarding school and learned from a phone call with Steve that Louis was too ill to teach and that Mr. Saunders, the toughest teacher in the school, had taken his place. It was funny, Steve said, but Louis's students found themselves remembering his classes with fondness, and how you'd feel good when Louis offered you praise, and how they were sorry they had once treated him so shabbily.

Steve also said his father had dropped by to have a few words with my father. Steve said that Big Jimmy had been talking with Doc Robertson and learned that Louis was expected to die in a few weeks. Big Jimmy said maybe he and my dad could do something for Louis, some gesture of thanks or acknowledgement. Big Jimmy had asked around and found a surprising number of parents who said this guy Zagar had really done something and they should do something for him. Didn't have to be fancy, just something he'd appreciate.

"Your father told my dad he knew just the thing," Steve told me.

What was that?

"Dad didn't say."

I didn't think about Louis Zagar again until I arrived home, and I didn't connect Louis Zagar to my mother's comment that dad and some men had been going out a couple of nights a week in December "to do guy things." Indeed, I didn't know anything until Christmas Eve.

We did our traditional readings of Dickens's *A Christmas Carol* and Clement C. Moore's *A Visit from St. Nicholas* and then my father announced a new piece of prose to be read aloud, Dylan Thomas's *A Child's Christmas in Wales*. It was my first exposure to this classic and it was terrific. My father said there'd be one further itinerary change on this Christmas Eve, and that I should go get my coat.

"Just the men tonight," he told my mother.

We got into the car and drove to the Presbyterian church. The parking lot was full of cars and a crowd of men were standing in the middle of it, stamping their feet and blowing vapour in the windless cold. One of the men had a young boy with him.

My father said I could stand on the street in front of the church but that I had to be quiet. I went around to the front of the church and waited.

It was a picture-perfect winter's night, the snow glistening under a full moon. The stillness made my ears ring. Looking around to see if anyone was awake on the street, I realized I was standing across from the house where Louis lived in his upstairs apartment. The blind on Louis's window moved and went up. I saw Doc Robertson open the window a couple of inches, then disappear. He reappeared a moment later in the downstairs doorway, hurried across the street, and disappeared behind the church without saying anything to me.

All was quiet again.

I looked up at the moon, then down at my feet, then up at the moon again.

I heard singing.

They came around the corner in single file, each holding a single white candle, cupping a hand before the flame. The young boy was leading them, his pure soprano riding high over the tenors, basses, and baritones.

I saw my father and Big Jimmy. I saw Mr. Donald and Mr. Tryon and Charlie Davidson. I saw Mr. Spicer and Mr. Farrell and Dr. Smith and Doc Robertson and Dr. Church the osteopath. I saw Mr. Leatherdale and the police chief and John Taylor, the Jewish motel owner. I saw Mayor Campbell and J.W. Park. I saw Tony Figaro and most of the male teachers from the Mariposa District Collegiate and Vocational Institute. In all, there were at least forty men and they were singing something sad and slow.

They lined up four rows deep in front of Louis's apartment. The young boy stepped forward and they all began to sing a rollicking song in a foreign language. It was, I later learned, a favourite of the Hungarian resistance fighters, a song of victory sung round the fire.

The young boy turned and walked to where I was standing. Seeing his face, I realized it must be Tony Figaro's son. We watched the choir—for this was most certainly a choir—as it began a hymn I'd heard in church, "All Through the Night." Save for the flickering of candles and the men's shadows dancing along the walls of the church behind us, all was still. The voices rose and sank and then soared on the melody. There was no movement in Louis's window.

Finally, they sang "Land of My Fathers." Their voices were into it now, pushing the song higher and higher in the night. The last verse was sung in Welsh. Their faces red, their voices straining at the melody, the forty sounded like four thousand.

As the magnificent last notes faded away through the bare branches and an echo died somewhere down the street, the men stood motionless. Then they turned and filed one by one the way they had come. Doc Robertson came back and went into the house. Nobody waited for him to come out.

My father and I didn't talk in the car. I could see his eyes were moist.

We learned on Boxing Day from Doc Robertson that Louis Zagar had died late on Christmas Eve. I don't know how much of his beloved songs he'd heard, or if he'd heard them at all.

I like to think he did, though. I like to think he was smiling.

He once told me that songs mean spirit. If our little town had broken away for a few moments and soared in celebration of his lovely music, a man like Louis Zagar would have to smile at such a lovely thing before turning to face the darkness.

Good Time Charlie

THE NEXT HOUSE on the waterfront has changed from a postcard-pretty little white-and-green-shuttered home to a larger brick-fronted Cape Cod-style house and garage extension. As a former newspaper carrier for the street, I remember the original house and its owner.

No chance I'd forget the owner. To quote Dickens, "He knew how to keep Christmas well, if any man alive possessed the knowledge." Boy, did he ever.

This was the home of Charlie Davidson. Better known as Good Time Charlie Davidson. Best known as the originator and keeper of Good Time Charlie's Annual Christmas Bash, the highlight of the Mariposa business community's year.

To appreciate Good Time Charlie's Annual Christmas Bash, you first have to appreciate Good Time Charlie himself.

Begin with the voice. Make it deep and brassy. Above all, make it loud.

Charlie Davidson didn't speak. He trumpeted.

He wasn't the loudest of Mariposa's business and professional community. That honour belonged to old Doc Hipwell, who boomed and rattled as if he had a gravel-coated megaphone in his throat. Everything Doc Hipwell said, he said in capital letters.

Doc Hipwell had the advantage over Charlie in that when people heard Doc speak it was usually in ideal speaking conditions. In the small waiting room in his office for instance, where people silently wondered what was wrong with the person next to them. Doc would greet his patients and inquire after their infirmities.

"HELLO FRANCINE! PREGNANT AGAIN? YOU OUGHT TO HAVE THAT HUSBAND OF YOURS FIXED!"

Or, "HELLO BOBBY, YOU GO RIGHT IN AND DROP YOUR PANTS. I'LL GET THE GLOVES!"

The other occasion to hear Doc was Saturday afternoons in the summer when he'd appear on the shore of his waterfront house and wade out into the water for his weekly swim.

"JUMPING JEHOSHAPHAT, THAT'S COLD!" he'd say, and everyone within a mile of the lake would know that it was two o'clock and Doc was taking his swim.

Swim is perhaps too strong a word for Doc's Saturday afternoon ablution. What he did was wade out until the water was above his waist but below his sunken chest and then stand there for an hour or two. Sometimes he'd splash water on his torso, and every once in a while he'd drop down until the water came up to his neck.

He never got his head wet. He never actually swam.

He didn't know how.

He'd just stand there, wave and yodel hello to passing boaters, and offer general comments on the weather or politics to anyone with their waterfront window open.

The old buzzard had remarkable eyesight, too. He'd see a kid such as myself wading into the water a quarter mile away and bellow, "HIYA KIDDO! HOW'S THE INFECTION TODAY?"

By contrast, Charlie was merely loud anywhere and in any circumstance and did not require the measured hush of a waiting room or the superb sound transmission characteristics of a lake on a summer afternoon to make himself heard.

Charlie was short and fairly wide, and his clothing ran toward loud chequered coats and wide garish ties cinched below an almost child-like face. He wore his black hair slicked back in the precise combings of a boy, and sported black horn-rimmed glasses of such thickness that his eyes seemed set in watery ponds.

While any town might boast of someone who looked like Charlie and talked like Charlie, it's unlikely any town had anyone who acted like Charlie. He did things in a way that were unfailingly original.

Take the manner in which he purchased a side of beef.

Every autumn Charlie would dress up in a hunter's hat and hunter's jacket, load up the back seat with empty beer bottles, and prop a rifle up on the car seat. He'd drive out to the Drury farm in the township and purchase an entire cow. The farmer would dispatch the cow with a single shot from the farmer's rifle and together the two would hoist the carcass up on the roof of Charlie's car. Then Charlie would drive south in the direction of the city.

He'd pull up to a suitable gas station in one of the suburbs—a station that had lots of people hanging around—and have the attendant fill up the tank. The attendant could hardly fail to notice there was a dead cow on the roof and that Charlie was dressed in the garb of a hunter. Pretending to notice the attendant's interest, Charlie would speak in what he imagined to be a middle European accent.

"Yimmeny, yes, she's a beauty. People tell me she's hard to shoot a moose but she's not so hard. She come right up to the fence and I shoot her good."

He'd pay for the gas and drive off, secure in the knowledge the attendant or someone at the gas station was already reaching for the phone.

When the inevitable cop pulled him over a few minutes later, Charlie claimed moral injury.

No, of course not, officer. I wasn't hunting. I bought that cow. Here's the sales receipt.

I'm wearing these clothes because of the chill. The gun has never been fired. There's no ammo in it, or in the car.

The beer bottles? They're empty and sterilized. My wife uses them to put up her vinegars.

No law that says a man can't drive home with a cow on his car, is there?

And of course the cop could find nothing illegal and would turn red and order Charlie never to darken suburban roads again.

As for the cow, it went into Charlie's remarkable basement. On one side was his wood workshop, a neat and tidy area with every tool imaginable on the wall or neatly stowed in drawers. The other side, separated by two layers of heavy hanging plastic, was what he called the meat shop. There was a meat locker, freezer, fridge, curing closet, industrial sink, saws and cleavers, an array of sharp knives, and a special drain in the floor hooked up to a septic field he'd installed under the backyard.

Charlie did his butchering in the basement. He said it was satisfying to hack up a carcass into cuts and make his own sausages and cured specialities. It was especially satisfying on Wednesday evenings, Wednesday being wife Flo's bridge night.

Flo's card cronies would show up and find Charlie opening the door, his arms and apron covered in blood and fat and tissue.

"Why Dorothy, come on in. I was just cleaning out Mother's ears."

Or, "Why Ruby, what a pleasure. I was just lancing Mother's boil," and Flo would rush up and scold him and shoo him downstairs.

Charlie was forever trying to make leather goods from the cowhide but the tanning process eluded him. All he ever managed to make was a single lumpy leather bag that looked like a boiled pancreas, although Charlie swore it was a perfect replica of a Norwegian tobacco pouch and he was only sorry he smoked cigars and not a pipe and so could not use it every day.

Charlie ran the insurance agency on Simcoe Street, just down from the police station, and he was a member of everything in Mariposa. He led the pledge to "The Roast Beef of England" on St. George's Day and the toast to immortal memory on Robbie Burns Night, wore shamrocks and carried a shillelagh on St. Patrick's Day, and cooked hot dogs and announced lineups at the annual Fourth of July softball picnic in Mariposa Beach Park.

Charlie was technically a Presbyterian, but he attended most of the town's churches at one time or another during the year. Sometimes he'd show up among Flo's Baptist congregation, sometimes at St. Paul's United. Occasionally he would attend mass at Guardian Angels up on the hill, but he seemed to favour St. James Anglican Church above all others.

St. James, he said, had the best choir.

Charlie would quiz the various ministers and priests the week before a service to ascertain the hymns they intended to sing at their next service. "Some of these jaspers," he'd say, "sing because they think they have to. I want a church where people sing because they want to."

Every few months or so he'd journey to the city and attend prayers at a north end synagogue. "I like the sound of the language," he said.

None of this marked Charlie as different or eccentric in Mariposa. Just about everyone had to belong to the same organizations if they were to be kept going in a small town. As for his service-hopping among churches, it was seen as something Charlie liked to do and was therefore acceptable.

People who are not from small towns often think them restrictive places, narrow in scope and short on tolerance. Quite the contrary. It didn't matter much what you did or what

you said or the faith you followed in Mariposa so long as everyone knew about it. Once the town understood just what it was
you did or said or believed, it was accepted. It was only when a
person changed what they did or said or believed that tongues
would wag, and the process of acceptance would begin again.

Besides, as the Presbyterian minister said, Charlie acted as
a seal of ecclesiastical approval. If Charlie shows up at your
service, the congregation knows it's going to be a good one.
Charlie wouldn't be there if it weren't.

What set Charlie apart in Mariposa was his Christmas office
party.

On the last working day before Christmas, the insurance
business would close early. The green louvred blinds on the
windows and door would be lowered and closed, a message
to all that commerce had paused to mark the birth of the
Christ child.

But closed in a small town mustn't be used in any narrow
big-city sense of the word. The *business* was closed, it's true,
but the *office* was open.

All afternoon a steady stream of small groups of men and
women could be seen making their way along Simcoe Street
and slipping into the insurance office through the front door.

The lawyers were always first to arrive on the scene, led by
crown counsel and trailed by the judge, magistrate, and justice
of the peace. They were followed closely by the doctors. As
professionals, they were expected to be prominent in any com-
munal venue, particularly if the venue included a tended bar.

They were followed in no particular order by the mayor, the
town clerk, a smattering of high school department heads and
elementary school principals, bank managers, and a flood of
business and store owners. There were the nurses from the
public health clinic, the librarian, and every reporter and editor who could slip away early from the newspaper office across
the road.

Round back in the alley behind Charlie's office, activity was hectic. Waiters crossed and re-crossed the alley carrying steaming covered trays between Charlie's back door and the rear door of the Golden Shangri-La restaurant.

Sales representatives from the distilleries and breweries unloaded station wagons, wheeling in cartons that clinked when they bumped over the doorstep.

Reverend Dawson, the United Church minister—known as The One Who Drank—used the back door himself, pausing to look reverently upon the stack of cartons waiting to be trundled inside. The Salvation Army captain, whose work took him daily to the courtroom and jail and county beverage rooms, breezed in the front door as if he owned the place.

At precisely 2 PM, the door of the police station would open to reveal the chief of police, resplendent in dress uniform with gold buttons and braids of office. He strode along the sidewalk and turned in the front door of Charlie's closed-for-business office.

Moments later, the constables and staff sergeants would appear on the sidewalk, split up into teams, and in two-by-two standard cover formation simultaneously enter Charlie's office from the front and rear entrances, followed immediately by the fire chief.

Good Time Charlie's Annual Christmas Bash was officially under way.

It was a mystery to me what went on in there even though my father was a regular. I couldn't ask about it. In a small town, if you have to ask, you don't need to know.

It wasn't until I was fifteen that I was able to attend my first and only Good Time Charlie's Annual Christmas Bash. I had dropped off some high school sports stories at the paper just as a group of reporters was leaving. One of them called out to me that they were off to Charlie's office and I should tag along.

I knew the reporters wanted to see the publisher's son kicked out of Charlie's for being underage at a place where alcoholic beverages were being consumed—reporters being the kind of folks who get a kick out of such things—but I didn't mind. It would be worth the embarrassment.

We came through the front door of Charlie's office and were met with a blast of warmth and noise. Charlie greeted us and, spotting me, immediately sized up the situation. He leaned in and growled, "If you want to stay, you'll have to look busy. Better clear away some of these dishes."

So I worked the party as a bus boy, removing plates and glasses, fetching drinks—a lot of drinks—and confined myself to drinking in the surroundings.

Here was old Fred Trefell, the man who played Santa in the Santa Claus parade, dressed in his Santa outfit and pounding out a number on the piano, pausing only to wave a tumbler of scotch at someone.

There was Mayor Campbell, discussing wines with Farmer Hodgins, the town bootlegger, and J.W. Park. Here was the fire chief discussing Egyptian cotton with the Jewish clothing store-owner. There was the head of nursing at the hospital telling an off-colour joke to a clutch of bankers.

Here was everybody who was anybody in town. Here were the people who made the town and its activities go. Nobody was drunk, but nobody was completely sober either.

Charlie set the tone, starting a conversation in one corner, then moving on like a firebug and igniting another somewhere else. He saw that everyone had the appropriate drink. He saw that everyone had all they could eat of such traditional yuletide fare as sweet and sour pork and egg roll and shrimp in lobster sauce.

He got everyone singing carols together, beginning with "Deck the Halls" and "Hark! The Herald Angels Sing," then moving on to such other traditional Christmas classics as "The Sidewalks of New York," "I Belong to Glasga'," and "Show Me the Way to Go Home."

With Charlie around, you had to eat and sing and drink and tell jokes all at the same time, and everyone did. Even the town bore—Magistrate Sims—was taken care of as Charlie had assigned the new junior partner at a law firm, a fellow named McCracken, to stand next to the magistrate and take the brunt of his Second World War stories. (Which did McCracken some good weeks later when, pitching a hopeless drunk-and-disorderly case, he said the affair reminded him of Dunkirk, and Magistrate Simms—having been at Dunkirk—agreed, letting McCracken's client off, thereby establishing the lawyer's reputation.)

In my many years of covering events since that Christmas party, I've heard the term "fellowship" used in connection with all manner of meeting and congregation, but Good Time Charlie's Annual Christmas Bash was the only one where the word truly applied. The rooms were awash with the stuff.

Later, around dinner time and after the last partygoer had left and I was clearing away tables, Charlie asked if I could be his Santa's helper for a few hours. I said sure, telephoned my parents to tell them I'd be late, and piled into a car with Charlie, its back seat stacked with presents.

We went to the Mariposa Retirement Lodge up on Old Muskoka Road, where he put on a Santa suit and talked to the residents—he knew all their names without asking—and handed out presents. Two blocks away, we stopped at the house of foster parents to a half-dozen special needs children. Again, he knew them, they knew him, and there were presents for all.

Then a long drive down a dark concession road where we turned off the lights and parked a little distance from an untidy, rundown farmhouse. Charlie got out of the car and, walking quickly and quietly, deposited six large presents on the dark doorstep.

He walked back a little distance until he felt he couldn't be seen clearly from the house, then produced a string of sleigh bells from his pocket.

He jingled them.

The door creaked open and light from a single bare kitchen bulb illuminated a small boy. The boy saw the gifts at his feet, yelled, and was joined by five older kids who roughly pulled the presents inside and slammed the door.

"Even when she's home, their mother's not all there," Charlie said. "Daddy's in jail. Those kids don't have much luck."

Our last stop was a red brick house down by the train station near the scrap yard. Word around school was that the house was a brothel.

Charlie flicked on the interior light, reached into the glove compartment and withdrew four cameo brooches. We wrapped them in coloured paper on the dashboard and placed them in an empty box, along with two bottles of champagne. Charlie opened the car door.

"It's a terrible thing to be lonely at Christmas, kid. You want to remember that."

Charlie put the box on the veranda, rang the bell, then hustled down the steps and into the car and drove away before I could see who answered the door.

Flo had decorated the tree and had a fire going when we arrived at Charlie's house. They asked me to stay for a late supper but I said I had to get home. Outside, I turned and looked at their house. I could see them through the living room window, sitting next to one another on the sofa, her hand in his, Charlie recounting the day's events, Flo smiling, happy in one another's company.

I was standing in that same spot on the sidewalk right now, but there was nothing to see.

Years after that night, when I was working in Vancouver, I got a note from an old *Mariposa Daily Packet & Times* staffer saying Charlie had died. He enclosed the death notice and a short news item from the same edition of the paper.

Charlie Davidson died on the last working day before Christmas at the Mariposa Retirement Lodge up on Old Muskoka Road where he'd been a resident for sixteen months. His wife, Florence, had predeceased him. The couple did not have any children.

The other clipping—a four-sentence police item—was as follows:

Three senior citizens were arrested for allegedly creating a disturbance on Simcoe Street near the police station on the afternoon of Dec. 23.

According to a police spokesman, the three—identified only as a former school principal, a retired merchant, and a former head of nursing at Soldier's Memorial Hospital—refused a constable's order to refrain from singing in front of an empty office building on Simcoe Street.

The three were taken into custody, charged with public mischief, and released on their own recognizance. They are scheduled to appear in Magistrate McCracken's court next week.

Folkies and the Old Folks

AFTER CHARLIE'S HOUSE come two anonymous houses built on what had been one large property with a single two-storey house. It comes as no surprise that the original yellow brick house is gone. It was old and weather beaten and a residence from another time.

Still, the home of Ruth and Casey Smith and their four kids—David and Bruce and Nancy and Barbie—had been a special place. For everyone.

For me, accustomed to playing in a sandbox and climbing trees and taking part in other small boy pursuits, the Smith house was Halloween and *MAD* magazine and autumn carnival rolled into one.

The adult Mariposa view of Ruth and Casey can be summed up in the story of how my parents renovated our attic to make a room for me and decided to christen it with a beatnik party. They invited all the parents on the block to come dressed as beatniks. Everyone did just that, showing up wearing beards and turtlenecks and berets and carrying bongos.

Ruth and Casey Smith came as themselves.

Their house was full of records by artists with names like The Weavers and The Kingston Trio and Odetta, and Ruth was the prime mover in the creation of the Mariposa Folk Festival. In the festival's inaugural year, the Smith home and property was turned into a bivouac for festival artists, with folkies in sleeping bags on the floors of the house and strewn the length of the yard all the way down to the lake.

I was far too young to attend the festival, but I remember it vividly because along with David and Bruce—the two Smith boys—I collected beer bottles from the Smith place and nearby Mariposa Beach Park all weekend. The three of us split a small fortune when we cashed them in.

It was while picking up empties early in the morning at the Smith house that I tripped over a sleeping bag containing a young woman and a young man. The young woman's name was Sylvia Fricker. The young man's name was Ian Tyson. Two years later, Ian and Sylvia released their version of Ian's song, "Four Strong Winds," the best song ever written by a Canadian about Canada. That's probably a bold statement, given the likes of Neil Young and Joni Mitchell and Gordon Lightfoot and The Band and too many others to mention, but I'll stand by it.

Even without the festival or Ian and Sylvia, the Smith house was unique. It was, for instance, an open house.

Any kid from the block—or anybody from anywhere—could open the battered screen door, walk in, and make themselves at home. Make some toast with jam or peanut butter from the convenient and ever-present pail-sized containers in the kitchen. Have a glass of milk. You weren't asked who you were or what you were doing there; it was assumed that since you were there, you belonged.

In a way, we all did. Ruth and Casey saw to it, even if they weren't always around.

The interior was spectacular in a rundown kind of way. Enormously high ceilings and a central hall where you could play touch football without anyone telling you not to. A living room that sported a sixteen-foot spikey balsam Christmas tree with its lights on from December through to March, and a full-sized pool table. The room was able to swallow them up and not feel cramped.

The bedrooms were different, too.

The boys' rooms were upstairs. Bruce's was a rat's nest of clothes and clutter and whatever woodworking project he was pursuing. A small boat, say. It was a remarkable mix of tools and car and nudie magazines, and that Bruce could get away with taping *Playboy* pinups to his wall at age fourteen was, to my mind, a real advance in the frontiers of humane parenting.

David's room was more studious and sedate until you came to know he had built a secret chamber behind a wall, accessed by crawling under his desk and removing a secret panel. Inside his fortress of solitude could be found such youthful treasures as Flash and Batman and Superman comic books—David was a DC comics man—and paperbacks by authors with names like Isaac Asimov and A.E. van Vogt and, the envy of any kid who ever dreamed of a chemistry set, a large scientific vial of pure mercury which you could open, pour out a few healthy drops, and roll them around with your finger without anyone telling you you were handling and breathing poison.

The girls' rooms on the main floor seemed to have more lace and frills than the other bedrooms, but they were pretty messy too, as you might expect of a couple of tomboys.

But the standout to me was Casey's bathroom. It had floor-to-ceiling bookshelves filled with the works of Lin Carter and L. Sprague de Camp and dozens of Ace Double science fiction paperbacks by the likes of John Brunner and Andre Norton and Clifford D. Simak, and adventure stories with heroes like John Carter and Tarzan and Conan. It's an unlikely idea of kid heaven, an adult's bathroom with bookshelves, but that's what it was to a boy fascinated by Mars and Africa and spaceships and dinosaurs and time machines. Entire days were lost in that room by boys sprawled on its floor, eating toast-and-peanut butter and reading themselves into far-away worlds.

It was a house where there didn't seem to be any rules—appropriate for a family with a father who, at the time, was the only psychiatrist north of Toronto—where the kids ran free, and parents were sometimes seen but rarely heard. Kids loved it and their parents hated it, fearing that the lack of parental discipline would eventually lead the Smith kids—and their own—down a deeply descending path to bad grades, pool halls, and basement jazz clubs. Maybe some kids did take that route, but it wasn't the Smith kids. However different their childhoods might have been from the rest of us, they grew up to be solid citizens. Parents. Achievers. Some of them even stand in public and announce their intention to vote Conservative. Turns out parenting is an art—and can cheerfully and gainfully involve a lot of folk songs.

Next to the Smith property was the grand and palatial Bowman house, a stone beauty that would have been right at home in Toronto's Rosedale, nicely hidden from the street by a high manicured hedge on the crown of Bay Street. The hedge is gone now and the house is fine, but it hasn't been kept up to its former standard. The next few houses are familiar—perfectly presentable and pleasant—yet hold little memory or meaning for me. I pass them by.

But then—occupying the last full block on the shoreline before you reach Mariposa Beach Park—here's the Willowmere Hotel.

Or where the Willowmere Hotel used to be. The Willowmere is no longer a hotel and hasn't been since owner Ernie Gadsby sold it. It is now, and has been for several decades, the Willowmere Seniors Residence. You can still make out the old brick hotel building, but the entire look of the place was changed with multiple additions, so that—with its absence of trees and greenery and its addition of abundant angled parking spots—it looks more like a motel than a seniors' complex.

In truth, however, the Willowmere Hotel was always something of a seniors' residence, only with fewer nurses, more reservations, and infinitely better food.

From late fall through the winter to late spring, the Willowmere Hotel was frequented by families and couples and travelling salesmen. But from late spring to early fall the hotel put on its summer livery, brought in its culinary experts, and was booked solid with well-to-do seniors who came north from Toronto and southern Ontario and Chicago and New York State and anywhere else large stashes of old money were to be found. If a guest came once, they'd likely be back the next year for a longer stay. They kept coming back again and again until they couldn't anymore.

Elderly couples, yes, the occasional widower, certainly, but what the hotel seemed to attract most were gangs of women of a certain age who, having buried a husband or grown tired of exerting the effort to attract a new one, were settling in to enjoy the finer things in life.

The hotel was old, classy, and—in the summer—very expensive. The regular nightly rate tripled in June and September, and quadrupled for July and August.

Worth it, though. It was one of a kind.

To begin with, the hotel had lovely shaded lawns that faced the lake and were littered with comfortable cushioned chairs that were a joy to sit in and—every bit as important for the seniors—you could get out of them without a struggle. There were brocaded pillows on every ottoman, throw pillows on every window seat. You could reach out in any direction in the television lounge or the card room or the reading room and put your hand to a pillow with a pattern or a material that reminded you of a remembered stay at an elderly relative's mansion, only without the pressure or the obligation or the supervision.

There were fresh-cut flowers on every table and bouquets in every room. The rooms themselves were simple yet elegant, with large and easy-to-open windows to welcome in the lake breezes during the day and electric blankets to keep the same breezes at bay during the night. Instead of their regular fitful sleeps, guests discovered they were able to snuggle in and sleep deeply, the way they remembered sleeping as kids.

Ernie Gadsby was the polar opposite to Leacock's famous hotelier, Josh Smith. Where Leacock dressed Smith in loud chequered suits to drape his 280-pound girth, Mr. Gadsby dressed in no-nonsense suspenders over a white shirt, its collar buttoned but unadorned with a tie. He had looked sixty-nine since his forty-fifth birthday, and he still looked sixty-nine when his clock struck eighty.

His innate appeal to his guests—and particularly to the widows—was his quiet blandness. His face rarely registered anger or discomfort or disappointment. His public countenance was always the same, a look that said here is man of quiet loyalty, exactly the sort of look an aging woman would like to see on the face of her butler or her groundskeeper or her cook. Or her hotel proprietor.

Unlike the loud and highly vocal Josh Smith, Ernie was quiet and meditative. He didn't speak so much as murmur, and when murmuring, murmuring in a sympathetic but never sycophantic way.

Everything at the Willowmere was designed to make its guests feel comfortable, cared for, and content. Nowhere was this philosophy more evident than in the Willowmere's dining room and its breakfast, luncheon, tea, and dinner sittings.

Breakfast, Mr. Gadsby maintained, was the key to a guest's day. "Keep it simple, keep it top-drawer," he said. "You hook 'em early and you've got them the rest of the day."

Mr. Gadsby talked the talk of breakfast being the most important meal of the day, and he walked the walk by contracting with the likes of the Barnaby and Dainard and Drury farms, Effie the baker, and Xin Chiang the egg chef.

There might be a temptation to elevate Mr. Gadsby into the realm of innovator and early advocate of the farm-to-table movement decades before it became fashionable, but he wasn't anything of the sort. He was simply looking for the highest-quality food in a town located a long distance from the city's food distribution centres, so he had to buy local if he wanted fresh and authentic.

Mrs. Barnaby out on the Oro Concession Road was a widow with six sons and two hundred laying hens—Rhode Island Reds, White Leghorns, and Golden Comets, a hybrid of the first two. They were prolific layers and all summer produced large brown-shelled eggs with startling orange-yellow yolks. Mr. Gadsby arranged to have 150 eggs delivered by one of the Barnaby boys to the kitchen door every morning by 6 AM. No hotel patron anywhere on the continent had fresher or better eggs. Just to have two of those beauties—soft-boiled in china egg holders, or over-easy, or run out in a dramatic basted or sunny-side-up arrangement—got half his guests out of bed and down to the dining room every morning.

Mr. Gadsby believed the secret to purveying a good egg was consistency in cooking. He put a remarkable amount of effort into seeing that once a guest's preference was known—fried, scrambled, poached, soft-boiled, shirred, or coddled—it was delivered that way—perfectly—day after day. The way to do that, it turns out, is to go get yourself an egg chef, and that's what Mr. Gadsby did. He went to the Golden Shangri-La and got himself a cook who had never cooked an egg before.

The Golden Shangri-La—known to locals as the Shang—was the most successful of Mariposa's three Chinese restaurants. It was the biggest and best and it was all due to its owner, Jin Chiang.

Nobody seemed to know where or when Jin first landed in Canada, but he somehow found his way to Mariposa and opened a little restaurant in a rental space on Main Street. He did well enough to expand, buy the building, and turn it into a flashy Chinese-and-Canadian cuisine emporium. It was staffed by dozens of relatives. If you were a Chiang relative and between the age of ten and ninety, you were working at the Shang. Everybody seemed to do everything, and if the kitchen doors swung open, you could see busboys and waiters and cooks lined up at a long table, books open, studying. Jin insisted his relatives learn good English and proper Cantonese, and woe betide any of his extended family's kids who brought home anything less than an A from school. It was widely believed he didn't pay any of them very well, but their rewards would arrive long before heaven did.

Every Chiang kid who worked at the Shang found his university tuition was paid for. Every married employee found a cheque for a down payment on a good suburban house in an envelope on the day of their wedding. The number of doctors, lawyers, and accountants who began as employees at the Shang is legend. At times the place seemed less a restaurant and more an academic factory.

The restaurant was unusual for other reasons, too. For one thing, it didn't officially open until noon. Jin let the other restaurants have the breakfast and donut trade. His employees only worked one shift, and that was from ten in the morning until ten at closing, and he didn't want to add more hours to their load.

While the restaurant wasn't open until noon, the door was open at ten and by ten thirty every weekday there'd be one or two dozen business folks inside drinking coffee and tea and swapping stories and gossip. There was also a regular coffee klatch consisting of active and retired professionals and

Mariposa merchants who met at ten thirty every morning and called themselves the Ten Thirty Club. The club fluctuated between six and eighteen people, and Jin himself would sit down and join them from time to time. He prided himself on keeping up with the news of Mariposa.

As an outsider, Jin understood Mariposa better than most Mariposans, and he worked his advantages whenever he could.

He knew, for instance, that parents were always worried about their teenaged children, what they were up to and what trouble they might get into. Jin transformed a section of the restaurant into a teen hangout, with booths with individual jukeboxes and burgers and fries and cherry and vanilla Cokes. You wanted to sit down with the cool boys and girls in Mariposa? The Shang was where you'd do it, and on Friday and Saturday nights, it hummed. Hormones practically pooled on the sidewalk.

Outside of the teen fare, Jin didn't put much in the way of "Canadian Cuisine" on the Shang's menu. He left that sort of thing to the other restaurants. Instead, it was North Americanized Chinese dishes. The only exception to this—indeed, the only person who insisted on ordering Canadian cuisine at the Shang—was a man who was a regular in the summer months. A pianist by trade. His name was Glenn Gould.

Mr. Gould's family had a cottage on Lake Ossawippi and two or three times a week, Glenn would show up—usually with two or three others in tow—and order his customary Golden Shangri-La dinner of six Parker House rolls, an astonishing quantity of butter to slather on the buns, a well-done steak, and coffee. Sometimes he'd bring record albums, including his own recordings, and Jin would play them in the restaurant while the pianist ate.

Although Mr. Gould would often wear a long heavy coat and fingerless gloves to the table—even in July and August—Jin never saw anything odd about the man or his dinner order and never uttered so much as a word about any perceived eccentricity. To him, Glenn Gould was a classical artist—the highest of callings—and that made him a respected and honoured guest. The man who recorded Bach's Goldberg Variations in 1955 could ride up on an ostrich and hum loudly through dinner and Jin would still have the staff serve him steak and rolls and butter, even though none of these items were on the menu. Whatever Mr. Gould requested, Jin would provide.

So when Ernie Gadsby went looking for an egg chef to work from 6 AM until 9 AM at the Willowmere, the first person he went to see was Jin Chiang, he of the 10 AM until 10 PM staff.

What he was looking for, Ernie told Jin, was someone who could be taught to cook eggs properly and, once he knew how, could do so over and over again. He needed to cook bacon and sausage and ham, too, but it was a light touch with the eggs that mattered.

Jin thought a moment. "Uncle Xin," he said. "He works our wok and fry pan station at the stove. He's your man. Once Xin's cooked a thing, he can cook it forever. If he agrees to your hours—and so long as they don't conflict with mine—he'll be perfect."

Except Jin was pretty sure Uncle Xin had never cooked an egg that wasn't casually tossed into a chow mein dish.

Nobody knew Xin Chiang's real age. It could have been anywhere from sixty to ninety. He was tiny and wizened, and though he could speak English, he chose not to do so. Xin was saving his money to buy a new house in Toronto where he could retire with his wife, his daughter, and her husband, and where the latter pair could live and produce many, many grandchildren.

"The perfect egg man," said Mr. Gadsby.

Ernie understood that Jin would take a substantial tithe out of whatever Ernie paid Xin, so once Ernie's wife—herself once a top egg lady—demonstrated to Xin the techniques necessary in presenting the perfect egg, and after Xin proceeded to rattle off perfect egg after perfect egg in a demonstration of his cooking prowess, Ernie took Xin aside. He said he was going to make a monthly payment, equal to Xin's Willowmere salary, and put it in an envelope addressed to the Xin Chiang House Fund, and that no one need know about it except Ernie and Xin.

Uncle Xin smiled, gave a little bow, and said in perfect English, "That is indeed most acceptable."

Ernie now had a loyal egg man. As it turned out, Xin was also a dab hand at the breakfast meats, too.

Mr. Gadsby had wanted the best ham, sausage, and bacon to go with those eggs, and on a tip from Charlie Davidson, the amateur butcher up the street, he learned of Ray Dainard's farm out on Concession 8 near Coldwater. Ray was a pig farmer who didn't want to simply raise and ship the raw material to market, he wanted a piece of the secondary manufacturing action, too. According to Charlie, Ray's smokehouse produced the best pork products north of Toronto. Not only was the bacon from his pork bellies superb, he produced gammon bacon—a sort of back-bacon that tapered into regular bacon—from the hind leg. A single piece of Ray's thick and luscious gammon bacon was as good as a trip to London's Ritz, Charlie said, only with considerably less need for airfare or a Cunard ticket.

Ray's dry-cured country ham—from the acorn-fed Ibérico pigs he brought in and raised—was a rosy-hued thing of beauty that alone brought four ladies from Virginia to the hotel for a week every year, just to savour the ham and remember what the world used to be and to tell themselves stories of when they were girls with bright summer dresses and momma's brooch and handsome suitors and how life lay before them like a juicy peach on a summer's day.

At Mr. Gadsby's urging, Ray experimented with various old-country recipes and procedures until he was able to produce two kinds of sausages, a Toulouse-style link that was mild and juicy and reminded diners of Paris or a European grandparent, and a pork sausage patty for the Americans who remembered the heavily salted and spiced Sunday breakfast sausage of their youth.

Ernie Gadsby understood that what his clientele wanted most was food that reminded them of when they were young. They couldn't get their youth back at the Willowmere, but they could recall the glories of it. And pay Ernie handsomely for the memory.

Lunch was always simple and light. Homemade soups—including a jellied consommé that was as good as the cup served on the Orient Express—and salads and sandwiches that ran from cucumber and pimento to the overwhelming favourite, a sublime chicken salad.

Tea service—in the dining room or on the shaded lawn—was a selection of breads and jams and small cakes and sponges and local berries and clotted cream, courtesy the talents of Miss Effie.

Ah yes, Miss Effie. The Willowmere's baker. She was tall and thin and short-sighted and looked as if the slightest breeze might carry her away, but she was an artist at her ovens and her marble-topped pastry table.

She showed up at 4 AM and was gone by noon, but her efforts anchored every sitting of the dining room.

For breakfast, there was fresh bread. Just two kinds, white and raisin. The latter was magnificent, a meal by itself, but it was the white bread that everyone remembers.

Light yet somehow chewy, redolent with that fresh baked smell, it ticked everybody's box as to what bread should look like, smell like, and taste like. You could have it as toast but most guests preferred it just as it was, sliced, then slathered with butter—courtesy Mrs. Denise Holtby, who churned it fresh every day from the family's Jersey herd—and matched with the remarkable jams, jellies, and preserves of Mrs. Hortensia MacWatters, winner twenty-four years running of the jams and jellies competition at the Mariposa Fall Fair. Mrs. MacWatters, at the behest of Mr. Gadsby, put her winners into small jars that fit in the wooden holders that Mr. Gadsby provided so that each guest could sample a row of all eight of the Fall Fair winners at their table.

These same loaves of white bread did for the luncheon sandwiches. For tea, Miss Effie provided superb little cakes and chewy Chantilly meringues and cream puffs light as clouds.

For dinner, she prepared individual small sourdough loaves—from a sourdough starter that was rumoured to have begun life in the Yukon before Miss Effie was born—brought to your table right from the oven.

There's a staff story that on the one day Miss Effie was too sick to come to work, a substitute loaf was provided to diners. Story goes that the diners took one taste of the substitute fresh-baked bread, arose, dropped their napkins on the white tablecloths, and left the dining room broken hearted.

Dinner service, however, was the realm of JayCee.

JayCee was J.C. and J.C. stood for Jean Claude, unless you were a member of the Mariposa Police Department in which case J.C. stood for Just Corrupt.

JayCee was the Willowmere's summer chef. He was a part-time Mariposan in summer and a full-time card player and rake. It was always a three-to-one proposition that he'd make more than one court appearance a season as a found-in at some illegal betting shop, or discovered in an overly refreshed state at an after-hours drinking establishment, or simply found swimming in the company of a half-empty bottle and a full-sized naked woman at two in the morning in Mariposa Beach Park. He was lawyer McCracken's best customer.

JayCee was a bad boy. Always had been.

It didn't matter to Ernie Gadsby. JayCee was his man when it came to cooking and plating the Willowmere's dinner menu, and if that meant bailing him out once or twice a season, then that was the cost of doing business to ensure JayCee was in the kitchen for dinner service.

The Willowmere's dinner menu reflected Ernie's belief that his guests wanted terrific food that reminded them either of their childhood or of great meals they'd had somewhere else. As his clientele was uniformly North American, it meant North American-type dishes, and only the best would do.

There were a mere five entrées on the dinner menu, plus an occasional special.

Beef. There were steaks or prime rib from the beef produced by the Drury farm, perfectly marbled and dry-aged and cooked exactly the way a guest wanted to see it on the plate, courtesy JayCee's skill at the grill and roasting oven.

Pork medallions from the Dainard farm were plated in a to-die-for mushroom-morel-truffle sauce JayCee had mastered—and stolen—while apprenticing in the south of France.

Fillet of pickerel, a local white fish that was light and succulent when singed in butter and served with nothing but salt, pepper, and lemon, but which, when paired with JayCee's sauce—a shrimp and lobster and Pernod purée served in a small gravy boat—was a showstopper. It was Ernie's idea to serve the sauce on the side because most guests preferred not to mask the remarkable lustre and freshness of the fish, and when you dipped Effie's sourdough into the sauce, it was practically a course all its own. Two or three slices of Effie's bread dipped in JayCee's heavenly sauce and a guest was happily adrift and floating for the rest of the evening.

Roast Mariposa chicken. That's not a menu item you might normally linger on, but for a Willowmere guest who'd ordered it once, they'd order it again and again, and then come back the next year and order it some more.

The secret was the chicken. These were provided to the Willowmere—and to nobody else—at a whopping cost by the Fontana family of Warminster. The little village of Warminster was known for its corn—thick-skinned kernels that exploded with sugars in the mouth—and the Fontana family were primary purveyors of it, but they also raised specialty chickens.

Extremely special chickens.

Bresse chickens.

Bresse chickens come from La Bresse in France and are acknowledged to be the best eating chicken in the world. Their taste is unique because of the breed and because of what they eat and fatten themselves upon while free ranging around the La Bresse farms. Then as now, the adult birds are tightly controlled and regulated by the French government. You can't import their meat.

You could, however, quietly purchase a few Bresse chicks and quietly raise them. You just couldn't call them Bresse chickens.

What you could do, as the Fontanas discovered, was raise a few Bresse birds, make the Mariposa-area farm environment as close to the French landscape as possible—lime the fields, feed them on plump sweet corn and grain and buttermilk—and you had something closely approximating Bresse chickens in taste. The Fontanas built up a sturdy little flock and sold a couple of them every day of the summer season to the Willowmere, where they'd appear on the menu as Poulet de Mariposa.

They were gold.

Every guest who ate that chicken was stunned by what Jay-Cee and the Willowmere had put on their dinner plate. It was better than any chicken they remembered from any Sunday table or any picnic basket. It was the one edible that was better than anything they could ever remember tasting.

It was an expensive proposition for Mr. Gadsby to serve these chickens, but it solidified his clientele and his ability to charge top dollar in the restaurant and hotel. Besides, any leftovers were turned into that sublime chicken salad the next day.

Finally there was a macaroni-and-cheese dish. Guests wanted to remember their childhood and JayCee served it up— unctuous and rich in a four-cheese kind of way—in individual casserole dishes that you could mop out with Effie's sourdough.

There was a dinner special from time to time and it was whatever JayCee felt like making with novel ingredients that came the hotel's way. Sweetbreads, scallops, it really didn't matter. The average guest stayed a week and might try one special, but only after exhausting themselves on their favourites.

Everybody gained weight. Reedy old men and stick-like women gained weight. Everybody groused that next time, they wouldn't eat as much. And everybody abandoned that resolution after just one breakfast or one dinner. It was worth taking a winter cure just to get back to the Willowmere's table in summer.

That was the genius of Ernie Gadsby, and the Willowmere Hotel was his masterpiece.

I became an admirer of Mr. Gadsby the summer he called me in, sat me down, and said he wanted me to provide a service for the hotel's widows.

I believe I raised my eyebrows.

What he was looking for, he elaborated, was someone who knew boats, who knew the local waters, and could take his guests on an evening tour of the waterfront. Would I be interested?

You bet I would.

So for one late July and all of one August in the year before I went off to my final year of high school, I was brought into the world of the Willowmere, was able to sit in its kitchens and watch its eccentrics at work, and was paid to take a small group of guests out on the waters of Lake Wissanotti three evenings a week.

It's where I met a woman named Alice who told me a story. She called it a ghost story. I call it a Christmas miracle story. Whatever you want to call it, it changed me.

The Presence

AM NOT A religious person.

My father would have liked to have been a believer—he loved old churches, loved the choirs and the music and the history of it all—but because of his upbringing, or perhaps because he was handed command of a series of warships on convoy runs across the Atlantic beginning at the age of twenty-two, he was never able to believe.

My father was Toronto Unitarian. I had no idea what that was. He didn't either. He characterized the church of his youth as being exceedingly open minded. "If I asked the minister if a particular action or moral position was acceptable, the minister would say, 'It's okay, Jimmy. It's probably in the Bible somewhere.'"

My mother was prairie Anglican, which meant she was raised more strictly than a Roman Catholic. But her wartime service in the Women's Royal Canadian Naval Service, or WRCNS—the Canadian version of the British WRNS, known everywhere as "The Wrens"—and then working as a reporter in Saskatchewan knocked the strictness out of her religion. She kept the forgiveness and compassion components but dropped the adhere-or-burn parts. Life, she felt, was difficult enough without conforming to a tome assembled by careerists centuries after Christ met his Maker. Her philosophy was to work the highest and kindest aspects of your particular religion into your daily life, and call it done.

Accordingly, I was sent to Sunday school at St. James Anglican for a number of years but never attended church services. Came time for my confirmation and my parents sat me down and said I could be confirmed and go to church, but if I did, I'd have to go to church regularly. They were of the belief that you were either in a congregation or you weren't. There was no part-time option.

This little sit-down occurred on my thirteenth birthday, a glorious sunny summer day. The prospect of donning shirt and tie and jacket and roasting on a pew while the sounds of summer fun drifted in on the breeze . . . well, I don't think my response of "No thanks!" came as a surprise or a disappointment. They felt they could take off in the boat for the afternoon secure in the knowledge that they'd done their bit to keep me on the straight and narrow and that whatever trouble I might get up to in the future was of my own doing, not theirs.

Pretty much the same thing happened later when they sat me down again on my eighteenth birthday to tell me they were leaving Mariposa.

My father, as always, couched it in nautical terms.

"You're off to university in the fall. You're launched. We've fitted you out as best we could and prepared you for rough seas and smooth. You're your own master now."

He then proceeded to rattle off a litany of major life changes.

"Your mother and I are upping stakes. We've done our bit and now we're off to have an adventure. We're selling the house. We've bought a little cabin on 250 acres on the side of a small mountain on the shores of the Bras d'Or in Cape Breton. The cabin was built by Admiral MacMillan after he went to the North Pole with Peary. We'll live there in the summer, and it's the best sailing in the country. I'm having a little sailboat built, one with a comfortable cabin for overnights. Builder's a local chap. Marvellous guy—mad as a hatter of course—but he knows his stuff. We'll spend our winters in the Algarve on the Med, where it'll be cheaper to live in their off-season than in our own home here in Canada.

"We'll travel around Europe and walk the Roman roads and seek out the hill forts and barrows and passage graves we're interested in, and I'll do a little writing. If it all works out, if we live modestly and do everything we want to do, we should be able to ease into our graves with satisfied souls and about a dollar left in the bank account. So no inheritance, I'm afraid. It goes without saying that wherever we are, you'll be welcome any time, and we'll come see you once a year of course, but consider yourself launched as an adult.

"My only advice is to find yourself a job that you like to do and are good at doing. Don't worry about the money it pays. Life works out if you can wake up and look forward to work and the people in your day. Discover what you want to do and do it before settling down. And don't retire until you have something you want to do with your time. Lot of damn fools retire and don't know what to do with themselves. Enjoy your life and don't waste it. Okay?"

Um, okay.

"Right then. You're a good son. Should make a good man, too. Carry on."

My dad was a few months short of fifty when he retired. He and my mom had thirty more terrific years in Nova Scotia and Portugal and Spain and their myriad wanderings around Europe. It might not be everyone's cup of tea—pulling up stakes from the town where you lived for so long, leaving friends and family and accustomed routines to go have an adventure—but it worked for them.

But then they always were a pair.

They'd met when he was the editor and she was a reporter in Moose Jaw. Here's my dad writing for public consumption about their relationship and his recipe for a happy life:

On a private, personal level, this was an especially memorable time. For I had met a girl who seemed to share my curious mix of enthusiasms, and who saw nothing incompatible about books and boats, baseball and Beethoven. Obviously, anyone able to appreciate the nuances of the man in motion as used in the Edmonton Eskimos running attack or the envelopment in detail tactics of Nelson at the Nile, or who could at least sit still, as she had done, while these were expounded at length, had to have hidden depths, and after we had succeeded together in taming a family of baby muskrats to take bread from our fingers and had sat, hand in hand, through *Brigadoon* and *Henry V* and the *Warsaw Concerto* scene of *Dangerous Moonlight*, our troth was as good as plighted. All unseen, an endless vista was opening up, of years and years of happy home and family life and beats to windward in small, leaky boats; of freezing hockey rinks and dizzying hill forts; of Neolithic passage graves and wind-buffeted walks across rainswept moors in the wake of Agricola's legions; of blue seas and tropic sunshine and silent, snow-blanketed forests of pine; of malt whiskey in front of a snuggery fire. We were blissfully unaware of it at the time, but we were about to Live Happily Ever After.

Not all of us go on to find such happiness.

Not all of us experience that sort of domestic miracle.

Not all of us experience any kind of miracle. Miracles of any stripe are by definition rare, especially the religious ones.

Over the years I've learned that there are a small number of people who feel they've experienced a religious miracle in their lives, and some of them seem compelled to seek out a reporter or columnist to tell them about it, an action that inherently lessens the importance of it. But I've only encountered one person who, out of nowhere, willingly spoke about what happens when a person experiences an according-to-Hoyle miracle and fails to respond to it. I wasn't a reporter when I heard it.

I am not, as I've said, a religious person, and in my younger days I was not all that interested in anyone who was. But then I was told a story about a Christmas miracle, and how ignoring that miracle brought a curse worse than what the miracle cured, and I've never been the same person since.

It was told to me by a woman—a guest at the Willowmere Hotel—and seemed to come out of nowhere while we were drifting on Lake Wissanotti on an August night under stars and a crescent moon.

The part-time job Ernie Gadsby offered me at the Willowmere Hotel was right in my wheelhouse. Fire up the Willowmere's boat—an eighteen-foot lapstrake wood runabout with a folding soft top and 35-horse Evinrude outboard motor and room for the operator, a passenger in the shotgun seat, and six more on two bench-style seats—and take interested guests on one of two excursions offered after dinner on Tuesdays and Thursdays and Fridays, weather permitting.

The first excursion was a twilight one-hour run up and down the shoreline from the hotel, pointing out landmarks, interesting houses, and interesting lake craft and answering any questions with local information. Ernie's purpose was to get guests out on the water in some comfort and complete safety—it was a very stable boat—to enjoy the slanted rays of the setting sun along two miles of waterfront, and then disembarking and enjoying a good night's sleep. Good food and good sleep, that's what brought the old folks back year after year.

I took them up the waterfront past the old waterfront homes on Bay Street and the newer houses on the far side of Bayside, then turned around and retraced our route to the hotel. Then down the other way, past Mariposa Beach Park and the boat liveries and the big yachts at anchor around the municipal wharf.

The first time up the lakeshore, when every sight was a new one, was taken at a relaxed pace. A really relaxed pace. It was so slow that trolling fishermen in small boats—out to fish the evening rise—would leave us in their miniscule wake. The return trip was only slightly faster as it would prompt questions guests hadn't thought to ask on the first pass.

I quickly learned that local facts and local colour were the key to successful tour guiding. Being a story enhancer or exaggerator didn't hurt, either.

"That's the Smith house, the property that hosted the performers at Mariposa's very first folk festival. They say there were more sleeping bags on the Smith property that night than can be found on a holiday weekend in all of Algonquin Park."

Or you could just stick to the basic facts, no colour added.

"That's the home of Sam Donnigan, renowned Canadian illustrator and probably best known to you as a regular contributor of cartoons to *Playboy* magazine."

No enhancement necessary for the Donnigan house. Guests embraced and reacted to the facts. If there was a man on board, the mention would prompt a knowing smile. The women, however, were invariably vocal in their response

"It looks expensive," they'd sniff. "I suppose he's very well paid for that sort of thing."

Sometimes they were more direct with their editorial comments, and seemed to think Hugh Hefner himself lived along the Mariposa shore.

"I don't know how the municipality and the neighbours can put up with it. Shameful to have such a man in the community. Shouldn't be allowed."

Both sexes, however, seemed disappointed at the lack of Playmates on display, but then, as some would remark, the light was fading and it really was too late for any of the girls to be sunbathing on the dock.

The second excursion was solely for the purposes of puttering down to the Mariposa Beach Park bandstand—a two-storey hexagonal green-and-white-with-red-roof structure that looked like a little gingerbread pagoda from the water—to listen to either the Mariposa Silver Band or the Mariposa Kiltie Band—essentially the same ensemble in different garb—as they tootled such favourites as "The Syncopated Clock" and "The Merry Widow."

The music and the light from the little bulbs on the bandstand flickered out over the dark waters of the lake where we'd anchor or drift in the company of pleasure boats and the occasional gliding canoe, all enjoying the concert and the starry sky.

There were never as many guests on the concert run as took the popular scenic excursion. I suppose it was either too late or not of sufficient interest. Still, it was remarkable how those who did attend the little concert on the lake turned reflective and ruminative afterward. Beguiled, you might say. They'd talk of an event or a person in their lives—usually someone of the opposite sex—and, more often than not, spoke wistfully of their regret at a moment not seized.

Which brings us to Alice.

I never knew her last name or where she was from, but I gather she was a solo booking on a two-week stay at the Willowmere. On this particular night, she was the only one on the concert run. I had a full boat on the early run and it was while we were still some distance from the hotel that two of the guests spotted Alice on the dock and proceeded to warn me about her.

"There's Alice. Oh, poor you, having to take her in the boat. She's a loner. She's touched."

One of the women pointed a finger at her ear and revolved it in circles in the universal gesture of someone with a screw loose.

"She's doesn't talk to anyone. She's standoffish."

Great, I thought. One passenger for the concert and she's a fruitcake. It did not auger gales of merriment for the remainder of the evening.

I helped the disembarking guests up onto the dock, helped Alice—a slight woman with grey hair and grey skin, likely in her late sixties—into the co-pilot's seat, saw that she was settled, and we were off. Having plenty of time before the concert, I gave her a tour of the civic waterfront and the yachts. She displayed not one iota of interest.

I anchored in front of the bandstand just as the Mariposa Silver Band struck up their first number and I was about to settle into a long dry sojourn when Alice asked if perhaps we might drift rather than anchor.

"The breeze feels so nice. I really don't mind not hearing the music."

I pulled up the anchor and stowed it and we began to slowly drift.

"It's a pretty bandstand," she said.

"Yeah," I said. "It was a miracle they didn't pull it down when they put up the new aquatheatre on the other side of the park."

I swear I had nothing in mind when I added that we seem to depend on miracles to keep the good stuff.

"You know about miracles, do you?" she asked.

Well, no. It was just a figure of speech.

She put her hand over the side and let it brush the surface of the water in the manner of a woman lounging in a canoe.

Neither of us said anything for a minute.

"I was just thinking that I do know something about miracles," she said.

"Oh yes?"

"They're not always the best thing to happen to you," she said.

"Really?"

She regarded me in a way that said she was judging what she saw.

"Perhaps I should tell you about it."

"Sure," I said. "If you'd like to."

She thought for a moment, tried to speak once or twice, and then spoke with resolve.

"The best way to tell it is to tell it as if it were a story," she said. "Somebody else's story. I don't think of it as a religious story—I'm not religious—even if it involves a miracle. I think of it more as a kind of ghost story."

"Ghost story?"

"Yes. I think it *is* a ghost story, and I'll tell it like that, if that's okay."

I said that was fine.

The air was cool, the breeze was gentle, the crescent moon did not overwhelm the stars, and the Silver Band was playing Herb Alpert in the distance when she began. She spoke in a highly educated manner and used different voices for the different people in the story—a narrator, an old man, a mother, and a young girl.

I remember every word.

THERE WAS A Presence, she began in her narrator's voice.

Yes, a Presence. We'll call it a Presence. And what had been empty space was now filled with the Presence.

No eye could see it above the pinpoint twinklings that were the lights of vast cities. No instrument could detect it above the orbits of the winking satellites. Did you know that the satellites you see moving across the sky at night, if they show a continuous light they're working, and if they look like they're blinking, they're dead?

"Yes," I said. "The dead ones are tumbling in their orbit and aren't continuously reflecting sunlight back to us."

Smart boy, she said, and continued as narrator.

The Presence considered the myriad activities beneath it. It absorbed the comings and goings, the births and deaths, the words and the thoughts and the deeds.

It found what it was seeking and slowly spiralled down.

To a continent. To a country. To a city. To a house. To a room.

To a room with a little girl with red hair who was in the process of cutting out a Christmas tree from a sheet of green bristol board when she heard the doorbell ring beyond her closed door.

The girl heard her mother's high-heeled shoes clicking across the hallway tiles. She heard the sound of the front door opening, heard the muted rumble that was the voice of her great-uncle David, a voice that signalled that it was—after all the days of waiting—Christmas Eve.

The little girl put down her scissors. She could hear her mother talking to her great-uncle.

You're sure you don't want to come with us, David? her mother said. There'll be lots of people you know at the Robinsons, and even more at the club. Wouldn't you enjoy a night out with us, instead of babysitting the kid? We can still get a sitter from the service, you know.

What? said great-uncle David. And miss Christmas Eve with little Red? Wouldn't hear of it. Most fun I have all year. Why don't you and Bob forgo the revels of your club for a night and stay home with us?

Don't start with me again, David. You know Bob and I don't get out that much. Bob does a great deal of business at the club and this is a good chance for him. With my days at the store—trying to see that my girls don't rob me blind—and with meetings and classes at night, I don't get a chance to get out and let my hair down.

Leave your hair up, said David. Leave it up or let it down but stick around here for the night. You'd be surprised at what we get up to, the fun we have.

David, you're my uncle and I love you and I appreciate you coming over to babysit, but I'm grown up now. I'm not your little niece anymore. I'm not your little Red anymore.

I know, I know. Can't blame an old man for trying.

Stop with the old man routine. You'll outlive us all.

Well, that—as your second husband is so fond of saying—is the game plan. Now then, lead me to the fruit of your loins.

For God's sake, don't talk like that. And don't call the kid a fruit. She might not be like the other kids but she's still … oops, there's my cab. I'm meeting Bob. There's pop in the fridge and you know where the bar is.

Aren't you going to look in on Red before you go?

I'm late. Besides, she's busy with her cards. You'd think she'd buy cards with the money we make, but she's happy just working on those damn cut-outs of hers. Don't wait up for us. Gotta run, bye.

The girl heard the front door bang shut. There was a silence, then a soft sigh from her great-uncle. She heard the thump of his galoshes on the plastic boot mat by the door, and felt rather than heard his stockinged feet moving along the hallway toward her room.

She put down her paper and scissors, picked up the crutches that were propped against her desk, and levered herself to her feet to wait for the inevitable barked question.

Where's my pretty one, the one with the sun in her hair? His voice boomed outside her door.

In here, Uncle. In here, she said, just as she always said.

The door opened and her great-uncle stood beaming in the doorway. He was dressed as he was always dressed, in a tatty blue suit that seemed to hang in folds about him. His ruddy face beamed, his eyes were wetly bright, his head crowned by a white and unruly shock of hair.

Throw down your crutches and fly! he ordered.

The little girl obediently dropped her crutches, tensed her good leg, and leaped in a parody of a swan dive toward him. He caught her under her arms and swung her around in an arc. Then he hugged her and carried her to her bed.

Lord, you've been eating anvils again, he said, easing her down on the pillows. There'll come a day when I can't lift you anymore, and that day will be soon at the rate you're gaining weight.

I'm not gaining weight, Uncle. You're just getting older.

Lord deliver me from the directness of children, he said, flopping into the armchair next to the bed. Don't speak to me of age, my girl. You're getting old yourself. Come now, how many years are you?

Seven, Uncle.

Seven, eh? We'll, you've joined the locusts and plagues now.

What are locusts?

Biblical grasshoppers. Insects from the Bible and the seed catalogues. But enough questions. You know we don't ask Great-Uncle David a lot of questions on this night. We prop ourselves up on our pillows, light the candles—which I see you've already done—and listen as your great-uncle reads his unfashionable stories aloud.

I know, Uncle. I've got your books here. They're all ready for you.

I see them. Let's see what we've got. Hmm, *A Visit from St. Nicholas*. What else? *A Child's Christmas in Wales*. A little unsound in spots, but then you'd expect that from a Welsh poet. They are an erratic lot but they know their stuff. Loved the language, our Mr. Thomas did. Maybe we'll get to it later.

There's the old one, too, the little girl said. *A Christmas Book*.

Ah, yes. Edited by D.B. Wyndham Lewis and G.C. Heseltine. It's important for an old newspaperman like myself and a young newspaperwoman such as yourself to know the names. Gets the old noggin working. The book itself is very spotty and certainly obscure for these times, but it has some juicy Latin that sticks to the tongue.

Which one do you want to read first, Uncle?

This one, he said, reaching into his pocket and pulling out a worn, leather bound volume. Charles Dickens. *A Christmas Carol*. I think you're ready for the long stuff now, Red.

I know the story, Uncle.

Good for you. So you know the story and you know there's a little boy in here with a game leg. Like your own.

Yes, but he got better, didn't he?

The old man looked at her, then looked around the room at the neat rows of expensive toys on the far wall that never seemed to be used, at the clutter of open books on the desk, and the elaborate paper cut-outs of Christmas trees and stars and angels. He turned to her.

Tell me, Red. Do you think your leg will get better?

The little girl looked down at the blanket that hid her withered leg.

Mommy says there's always a chance, and she's always taking me to new doctors. They say there's a chance, but I can see it in their eyes, Uncle. I don't think there's any chance.

The uncle—a great lover of quotes and epigrams—remembered one of Oscar Wilde's rhymes:

All her bright golden hair
Tarnished with rust,
She that was young and fair
Fallen to dust.

Does it bother you, Red? he asked. Thinking it won't get better?

A little. Sometimes. Sometimes I wish I could be like the other kids, like Bob's first family. When they come over I wish I could play with them. Play hide-and-seek. They know I'm not the same as them. They know I don't talk the same way. They don't talk to me much. I'd like it better if they would, but I guess they're afraid of me.

Why's that, do you suppose?

Because I'm lame. Because I'm different.

As he had so many times before, the old man reflected upon the directness of the little girl, and her cheerful acceptance of what he called "the general rumness of life."

Well, never mind, Red. Let me tell you something. I'm an old man. It is the nature of old men, having done everything they set out to do in life, to see things quite clearly. See things the way they are.

When I was a young man, I looked at things the way young men do. I planned and I worked and I was caught up in my own world. It seemed a good world—and it *was* a good world, by and large—and I went my own way.

But when young men become old men, Red, so much of what they once took for granted is forgotten, or drops away like clothes that are no longer necessary. One comes to a more general view of things. One comes back to what one first learned. In my case, it means coming back to the theme of St. Paul—the man I told you about—and that is faith, hope, and charity. Not always popular or fashionable today but still very much worthy of our consideration, especially at this time of year.

If you can have a little of these qualities, Red—and I can see that you do—then you have what is best in this world. It is an unfair world, sometimes a cruel world, but you can do what you can do to make it a little better.

Which reminds me, Red, here are the cheques you asked for. One to the Salvation Army, one to Save the Children. You sure you want me to mail them for you? It's your Christmas present money, you know.

Yes, please, Uncle. I've made Mommy and Bob and you your presents. I don't need the money Mommy gives me. I know she doesn't like me to give it away, but I don't need it. Honest, Uncle.

You like giving it away?

I like giving people things, Uncle. It feels nice.

Yes. Doesn't it? It's all part of redemption, Red, the feeling of giving pleasure and comfort to others. And that, as it happens, is exactly what our friend Dickens here is on about in his *A Christmas Carol*. The blessing of this story is the great furnace of real happiness that fires old Scrooge and everything and everyone around him. It doesn't matter whether the ghosts of past, present, or future convert old Scrooge. What matters is that they convert us. So let us begin, shall we?

The time poured by slowly and easily. The candles threw dancing shadows on the walls, the snow fell softly outside the window, and the little girl listened happily as the old man read to her of Marley and Cratchit and Tiny Tim and the goose that was as big as the delightful boy. A world was created, unfolded in the room, and then lingered long after the book had been closed.

The old man read a little from the other books, and at last he fell back in his chair.

It's late, Red. Shall I leave you to your sleep?

No, Uncle. I'll go wait for Mommy and Bob so I can wish them a merry Christmas when they come in.

You know, Red, they might be late. They have been very late before.

I know, but I don't want to miss them.

Red, you know they come in rather... well, somewhat the worse for wear?

Sometimes they've been drinking. I know, Uncle. But I wouldn't want to miss them on Christmas Eve. I never have.

With that, the girl swung her legs out of bed, draped herself in her dressing gown, and using her crutches hopped out of the room and down the hallway to the bench by the front door. She sat down and waited, humming carols to herself.

The old man listened to her through the open bedroom door until she fell silent. He thought again of the general rumness of life, then soon fell back, asleep.

The Presence—motionless for so long—passed over the sleeping girl's leg.

Deep within the tissues, dormant synapses fired. Blood rushed into cells. The brown malignant stain receded.

The Presence moved away, spiralling up above the house. Above the city. Above the country. Above the continent.

No eye could see it above the pinpoint twinklings that were the lights of vast cities. No instrument could detect it above the orbits of the winking satellites.

Not even the little girl with red hair who was asleep when it brushed past her.

When she awoke, it was Christmas Day.

ALICE WAS SILENT, staring at the dark water. I realized the story was over.

We'd drifted down the shoreline and were almost in front of the Willowmere. I started the engine, idled in to the dock, and secured the boat.

Alice hadn't moved. She was still staring at the water, as if she had said all she had to say and now was looking for something—a response, an answer, anything—in its darkness.

Feeling I had to say something to snap her out of it, I thanked her for her story.

She jerked, recognized where she was, and collected herself. I helped her out of the boat onto the dock then jumped back in to the boat to tidy up.

Alice stood on the dock, looking off into the distance.

Still feeling I had to say something, and wanting to close it down for the night, I asked her if the miracle made much of a difference to the little girl's life.

"You'd think a miracle would make a difference, wouldn't you?" she said. "You'd think being in its presence would change everything. You'd think good things—and only good things—would be the result of coming through that remarkable, unexpected, and completely inexplicable happening.

"You'd be wrong.

"It would only work for you if you heeded the miracle's message. I didn't.

"The miracle led to nothing. Nothing but unhappiness.

"Loveless marriages. Failed dreams. Failed expectations. Cirrhosis. Clinics. Failed families. A world where you find you've driven your children away. A life of loneliness. No one coming for Christmas. No one to visit for Christmas. No more cut-out cards. No best wishes for a happy new year.

"No faith. No hope. No charity. No redemption.

"If you failed to read the meaning in that miracle, then what you're left with is my life. A life where the high point is to come to Mariposa for two weeks to eat and to remember how glorious the world once seemed before it all turned to mud."

Jesus. I didn't know what to say. The only thing I wanted to ask—so that I knew for certain—was who was doing the talking. I wanted to hear her say it.

"Are you...? Are you the little...?"

I couldn't say it directly. So I asked it a different way.

"Are you saying the little girl with the red hair squandered her miracle?"

Alice looked at me as if she was seeing me for the first time, and that what she saw was the saddest sight she'd ever seen.

"You don't understand," she said, shaking her head. "You don't understand at all."

She paused, and then uttered two short sentences in a tone so cold and so dead they were encased in concrete.

"I'm not the little girl," she said.

"I'm the mother."

A Wondrous World

I STOOD ON THE sidewalk in front of the Willowmere Seniors Residence, thinking about Alice, and reminding myself—for the umpteenth time since first I heard her sad story—to pay attention to the ordinary and the extraordinary things that pop up in the course of a life, when an elderly gentleman in a disreputable fishing hat deliberately nudged my leg with his wheeled walker.

"What are you staring at, young fella?" he demanded. "If you stand out here with your mouth open and that vacant look on your face, they'll be out with a net and have you inside in a flash."

I smiled. It had been a while since I'd been the recipient of the term "young fella."

"Are you a resident?" I asked.

"You bet," he said.

"Nice place?" I asked.

"Nice enough," he said. "I always somehow thought that once I'd retired and decently interred the wife that I'd be wearing a Panama hat and a bright-coloured tie and smoking a big cigar with an iced vodka in my hand on a balcony overlooking the Med. Tangiers, maybe. Or Gibraltar. Didn't happen, of course. Waited too long. But this place is okay. It's on the lake. I've got the park next door to go walkabout in. The kids and the grandkids are handy. So no complaints except old age."

Nice room?

"Nice enough. A little small, though. There ain't enough room in it to flog a weasel, but it does for me."

I wished him well. He tipped his hat and pushed on toward the park.

Me, I was thinking of his language—"decently interred the wife" and "ain't enough room in it to flog a weasel"— when I was suddenly back in the Golden Shangri-La amid the strange expressions and the full-throated chorus of the Ten Thirty Club.

The Shang is long gone now, turned into a pleasant pub and restaurant, and the members of the Ten Thirty Club are no more. It's likely they took their colourful language and their odd diction with them. In a PC world, innovative and memorable local phrasings and expressions are likely to be MIA.

But they're alive in my head, as is the clatter of the crockery, the smell of a small-town Chinese restaurant, and the sight of the old men as they enter and take their places.

They wipe their brows with sensible handkerchiefs in summer, stamp the snow from their galoshes in winter, blessing their souls and good gracious-ing and gawdamn-ing but it's never been so hot or so cold or so wet or so dry or so this or so that.

They settle into the two adjoining end booths according to a seating plan known only to themselves and fuss with their belongings and exchange pleasantries with their host, Jin Chiang, who pours them coffee before joining them. Another meeting of the Ten Thirty Club has begun.

The club is just one of the local chapters of an informal global brotherhood. Around the town, around the province, around the country, around the world, old men can be found settling themselves around a hot beverage to discuss the events of the day. They might be sinking into the soft chairs of an expensive private club or squirming on the hard seats of a coffee shop or squatting around a glowing brazier. The setting is as varied as the geography, but the purpose is always the same— to offer commentary and advice, to criticize and to complain, to pronounce and to sit in judgement on an imperfect world.

It could be the antics of a prime minister, the politics of a war, the erratic behaviour of a neighbour, the lack of milk from a previously productive cow—these clubs cast their nets wide, and rare is the day the catch is anything but plentiful.

The men in the Golden Shangri-La could have adopted the name of the restaurant for their club, but that would have exhibited favouritism toward their host at the expense of such popular spots as Pete Stover's place down the street or Paul Weber's little hamburger stand out on the highway. They could have called themselves something grand like the Athenaeum Club, but that would have been putting on airs. No, they declared themselves to be simple and straightforward men and so would adhere to their simple and straightforward principles and name themselves after the time of their meeting—the Ten Thirty Club.

Simple and honest and straightforward they might be, but they suffered no fools. I've heard them dismiss a US president in a word, a religion in a phrase, an entire society in a single short sentence. Not for them the tangled world of polite jurisprudence or international relations with its technicalities and nuances and evasions; either a club member must tell the unvarnished truth or keep his trap shut.

If something is amiss, it should be so stated. If a politician is an ass, better it be known. If the local priest got off a good joke at the service club luncheon, then a Protestant must manfully acknowledge the achievement despite the papal representative's handicap of birth in Ireland or his drinking habits or his questionable counselling of a grieving young widow.

Yes, a man had to tell the truth if he were to be a member, and Charlie Davidson told me as much the morning he brought me along to sit in on a session of his club.

It was the summer before I headed out for my final year of high school. He'd asked me over to help him clear the lake bottom next to his dock so the small kids of his wife's sister's family could wade without fear of sharp or inconvenient objects. After we'd cleared the stones and clams, Charlie determined suitable payment for my labour would be to invite me downtown to sit in the Shang and listen to old men critique the world around them.

Fair enough. The experience would prove more valuable—and lasting—than any monetary reward.

Come to think of it, it was at this morning session when I was introduced to a man who'd been a guest of the Willowmere Hotel for a season, a man I'd meet much later in life as one of the great professors at one of the world's great universities, and eventually, the source of an unusual Mariposa Christmas story.

His name was Eggs Kelly. He was the only visitor to be granted *ex officio* membership of the Ten Thirty Club, but that's getting ahead of ourselves.

It was a summer sitting of the club that I attended and thus the turnout was relatively sparse. Charlie had told me to drink my coffee and speak only when spoken to—and that probably wouldn't happen because, as Charlie put it, members had difficulty acknowledging any opinion other than their own, and if they ever did, it would only be grudging—but that I'd probably know most of the members.

I did. With only one exception, the members on this day were lifelong Mariposans.

There was Charlie himself, of course, beaming and loquacious and unable to abide a peaceful or tranquil moment without rushing to fill it. His favourite expression was "Christ on a crumpet!" Charlie, as the operator of the insurance agency, was the club's expert on international commerce.

There was J.W. Park, our neighbour and now retired owner of the town's largest car dealership. His inexplicable favourite saying was "Molly goes to Rome!" Nobody knew who Molly was, or why she was bound for Rome, but he said it so passionately that it seemed best not to inquire. He was the club's expert on technology, banking practices, and the Fallibility of Man.

There was Mr. Cunningham, the retired high school science teacher and director of its annual school musical. He confined his outbursts to "Golly" and "You don't say!" He spoke for the sciences and the arts.

There was Fred Terigo, the ancient retired linotype operator from the *Mariposa Daily Packet & Times*. His expression of surprise and amazement was "I near soiled myself!" As he was always surprised by what he heard and in a perpetual state of amazement, he was generally assumed to be incontinent. Fred had a grade five education and was the club's resident expert on organized labour and media practices.

There was Jin Chiang, the aging but still-going-strong owner of the Shang, whose favourite expressions were "No ways!" and "Phtooie!" Jin was the club's resident expert on immigration and foreign affairs. Thus, "Mao Zedong? No ways!" or "Mahatma Gandhi? Phtooie!"

As always, the meeting was chaired by its most vocal and least formally educated member, John Thompson.

Mr. Thompson was a large red-faced man with eyebrows in need of mowing and spectacular tufts of white hair shooting out of his ears, who had dropped out of school after grade three to work the family farm. He regularly ended his observations with the benediction, "An' if that ain't so, then my arse is a hoop." Mr. Thompson was the club's expert on education.

I would later ask my father about Mr. Thompson and was told that while his formal education was scant, he was likely the best-read resident in the county.

"Mannerisms, as well as appearances, can be deceiving," my father said. Mr. Thompson had read his way through the *Encyclopaedia Britannica* as a youth, followed it up with the entire Great Books series, and had read pretty much every non-fiction book in the Mariposa public library. He took a liking to Plato in his late teens and learned Greek so as to read the man in his own language. He subscribed to Sunday papers from New York, London, and Athens, as well as to the *Mariposa Daily Packet & Times* which, as my father had learned from long exposure to Mr. Thompson, he'd read carefully every day.

But in the realm of deceptive appearances, it was the man I didn't know or recognize—the one who attended only in the summer months and at Christmas—who topped the ranks.

Eggs, they called him. Eggs Kelly. Short, balding, and bespectacled, he looked younger than the others. He wore a perpetual beam that made him look like a pink-faced cherub chuckling over a private joke. Where the others issued comments loudly and often, he only spoke twice during the entire meeting, and then it was only to ask, in a meek and mouse-like way, if someone might kindly pass the cream. He did say something else in a soft voice I couldn't quite hear from my next-booth-over seat but whatever it was he said, it caused the others to lean in, listen, and nod their heads. I was old enough to spot deference when it was offered, and it was being served up here in a chalice.

I sat through the one-hour session and Mr. Thompson said I was welcome to drop in anytime. Walking home with Charlie,

I asked why everyone seemed to defer to Eggs. Charlie said I should attend Friday's meeting. It would be worth my time, he said, and all would be made clear. Get there five minutes early, though.

I arrived five minutes early on Friday to find the club assembled, convened, and attentive. Nobody was speaking. They were waiting for Eggs Kelly.

As the Presbyterian church clock chimed the half hour, the door of the Shang opened, and Mr. Kelly entered, carrying a briefcase.

He walked to the booth table and opened his briefcase. He took out a few pieces of foolscap. He turned the open briefcase on its side at the end of the table, placed the paper on top of this makeshift lectern, beamed at his small audience, then proceeded to address us while standing at the end of the booth.

It was, of all things, a lecture on the history of the cinema.

He spoke about the beginnings of film, and about the French magician Georges Méliès roaming the streets of Paris with his camera, accidentally inventing trick photography on the day his camera jammed. How the low-life New York peepshow operators took over the industry after film had been used by vaudeville theatre owners during an actors' strike. How the industry moved to Hollywood not for the weather but for its distance from New York and its proximity to Mexico so that when the Motion Picture Patents Company, an undisguised trust set up for George Eastman and Thomas Edison to control all aspects of film, sent its lawyers across the country after them, they could nip over the border until the coast was clear.

He spoke of David Wark Griffith—"D.W."—who largely invented the modern film with the close-up shot, ensemble acting, and chase scenes which, through the use of Edwin Porter's technique of cutting up pictures and pasting them together in a new order—a process called editing and *the* distinctive art of the cinema—altered people's sense of time. Of how actresses Clara Bow and Joan Crawford did more to transform women than all the suffragettes and activists combined. Of how film was the most powerful channel for societal attitudes yet invented.

I hadn't been to university yet. I had yet to hear Seamus Heaney lecture, or the young Simon Schama, or Stephen Jay Gould on the Burgess Shale, or the greatest of them all—W. Jackson Bate's lecture on the death of Samuel Johnson, to which professors and students flocked and left the lecture hall in tears—but I have heard little to top the lecture Eggs Kelly gave in the Golden Shangri-La all those years ago.

I was mesmerized. He used no pictures or gimmicks. Just words and ideas in an agreeable order. It was my first exposure to wit and erudition and learning as executed by an expert. This was my introduction to Donald H. Kelly, Harvard University Professor of American and European Intellectual History.

When he finished his lecture—just as the Presbyterian church clock struck the bottom of the hour—he beamed at us, returned his notes to his briefcase, and walked out of the restaurant, whistling.

It took me a few moments to pull myself out of the reverie he'd woven and when I did, it was to catch up to Charlie Davidson out on the sidewalk and pester him with questions.

As we walked home under the August elms, Charlie told me about Donald Kelly.

He was born in Mariposa, the only son of immigrant parents.

"They changed their name from Kalinski or Kainovski or some such Slavic name," Charlie said. "Don't know much about his early years, other than he was a bit of a loner."

Charlie first met him in high school.

"I was about the closest thing to a friend Donny had back then," he said. "I didn't spend too much time with him, mind you. I was a pretty popular kid and I wasn't lacking for friends, and I didn't bully him the way a couple of the others did. Most of our peers just ignored Donny, yet he and I seemed to get along. It was our first year in high school—grade nine—and neither of us was all that interested in school. I'm not sure what he was really interested in, but it wasn't school work."

In the summer before grade ten, Donald met a girl.

"Mary was quite a girl," Charlie said. "Very quiet. Hardly spoke. Pretty, too."

Charlie paused.

"She was Indian."

He paused again.

"She was one of the Indian girls from the Reserve across the lake who came to our high school. Bright. I mean, really bright. Course, none of us had much to do with her or her friends. Seems stupid and wrong now—hell, it *was* stupid and wrong. Still, it was the way things were then. Attitudes of our parents, visited upon us, I suppose. Excuses, excuses, excuses, I know, but real to us at the time. Though not to all of us. Not to Donny."

All through grade ten, Donald and Mary spent time with one another.

"Reading in the library. Walking in the park. Hand in hand. First kiss. First love."

"Donny ignored the snickers," Charlie said. "Certain amount of guts in that. Ignored the taunts, too. Stood up to anyone who said it to his face. That definitely took guts. Got beat up once, but he inflicted so much damage of his own that nobody took him on again. Anyway, he and Mary sort of dated, I think. Certainly spent all their time together. Donny didn't hang out with anyone else. All through grade ten and into the fall of grade eleven. And then, something happened."

Charlie stopped walking and turned to me.

"Donny wasn't the kind of guy to confide in anyone, but he gave me enough hints to know what happened.

"She met his parents and he met hers. Pretty sure it was on the same day. They hadn't told their parents anything and then Donny brings her home on a Saturday morning and introduces her, and they hop the bus to the Reserve and she introduces him to her parents.

"The result? The only thing I can think to call it was the term we used to use back then. It was a shit show."

Charlie began walking again.

"Donny's parents were real Old World types. They stuck to a small circle of their own immigrant friends, and I guess the thought of their boy seeing an Indian girl must have driven them half mad. Anyway, his parents said he couldn't see her anymore.

"Pretty sure her parents said the same thing to her. The Reserve was a closed community in those days. Red and white didn't mix, and her parents weren't about to buck the trend.

"But because Donny and Mary were both so quiet anyway, it was hard to tell anything was going on. But I know he was devastated. Just wasn't the same guy. And this is before Christmas. This is before the accident."

We were walking through Mariposa Beach Park now.

"Mary was babysitting for some family in town right before Christmas. Her father had borrowed somebody's beat-up car to drive her to the house, and then came back to pick her up real late. Rather than take the road around, they drove across the ice on the lake. Nothing unusual in that, but that was the year the Narrows ice changed."

"Narrows ice" is a term people around our lake understand. It refers to the current that runs between the two lakes, from the larger to the smaller, through the Narrows. In winter, it means the ice is thinner in the Narrows and for a couple of hundred feet out into our lake than it is elsewhere. The current keeps the ice from freezing as thick as it would anywhere without the current.

"Nobody knew it at the time but the current that summer had laid down a new underwater sandbar and it angled the current away from its traditional course and out to the right of the last starboard channel buoy. Where normally the ice was thin, it was thick that year. And off to the side about a hundred feet, where it's normally thick, it was thin.

"Mary's father drove on what was normally thick ice, only now it wasn't, and the car went right through. They didn't get the bodies out until the spring when the ice went out."

Charlie was looking at the lake now. It looked warm and placid and peaceful.

"At the time, it didn't seem to me that her death made that much difference to Donny. He was still quiet, still kept to himself."

Charlie stopped again.

"Funny," he said, "but now that I think about it, that was exactly the time when he took to the books in such a strong way. Must have been the grief. Whatever it was, he became a helluva student. Aced all his subjects. Highest marks in the school in grades eleven and twelve. By graduation, he was top three in the province. He won a scholarship in the States and took off. We didn't see him for a while. He went to Harvard, then taught at Brown, and then taught at Harvard. He's tenured now. I gather he is some kind of resident genius when it comes to the teaching of history, but I guess you can understand that, given his performance this morning," he said.

"But why he did he give us a lecture?" I asked.

"Donny comes home during the summer to write one or two new lectures and to re-write and renew all his old ones," Charlie said. "The result is that the Ten Thirty Club has pretty much taken the full load of Harvard's 'European and American Intellectual Histories, 1800-to-Present' courses. We're not the doddering old boneheads you might think.

"A few years back, I cut a deal with Ernie Gadsby at the Willowmere. I booked Donny into the Willowmere for July and

August at one-tenth the going rate. In return, Donny gave the guests one of his lectures once a week."

I said I hadn't seen Mr. Kelly at the hotel or around Bay Street.

"That's because he only lasted the one summer at the Willowmere. Said he gained too much weight. Said he still couldn't afford even the one-tenth of the Willowmere rate on his Harvard salary. Mostly, though, he said the older widows hit on him too much for comfort. So he took a cottage up the lake, and still does."

"Why does he come back at Christmas?" I asked.

"Don't really know," Charlie said. "He comes to dinner at our place on Christmas Eve, but otherwise, he just stays at the little winterized cottage on the lake. Takes walks. I really don't know."

"Why do you call him Eggs?"

Charlie laughed.

"That was John Thompson's doing. John didn't go to school, but he hung around the guys who did. He's the one who, when Donny started piling up the high marks, called him Egghead. Donny confronted John and said he didn't like the name. So John said, 'How about Eggs?' Donny said he could live with that, so he's been Eggs to us ever since."

I had a sudden thought.

"Was Thompson the bully who beat Eggs up?"

Charlie laughed again.

"No," he said. "It was a friend of John's who did. John straightened him out. Turns out John has some Ojibwe blood in him. That, plus you have to remember that John was reading books and studying on his own, so when Eggs starting studying for real and started getting the really good marks, that impressed John. He and Eggs have been loosey-goosey friends ever since. It's John's cottage that Eggs rents every year. It's John who Eggs spends Christmas Day with."

And that was that—until a year later, when I was home for Christmas and spotted Mr. Kelly walking along Main Street. It was late on Christmas Eve afternoon, and I was heading home. I remembered Charlie saying Mr. Kelly always had dinner with Charlie and Flo at their house, so I caught up with him and introduced myself.

"Ah yes," he said. "The newspaper publisher's son. I was working out the 'Silver Screen' lecture at the Golden Shangri-La when we met, if memory serves."

I asked if I could walk along with him to Charlie's house. He seemed startled by the request. Then he looked at me and said that I could walk with him, but he had to perform an errand at the St. James Anglican Church cemetery on the way.

When we reached the cemetery, an area of snowbound darkness surrounded by high hedges, he asked me to wait on the sidewalk while he went in. I noticed he was carrying a book. It had a grey cover with a large red ink stain on it. It looked to be some kind of old school book.

After five minutes, he emerged and stood beside me, watching the snow falling from the black evening sky.

"It's a wondrous world, this," he said. "I say it every Christmas Eve and I say it again. It's a wondrous world, indeed."

I said nothing. We walked to Charlie's house and we said good night and happy Christmas, and he went in.

It was getting late and I had to get home for dinner, but I turned and ran back to the cemetery. Peering at the snow on the ground, I found Mr. Kelly's footsteps. They led straight to a small flat grey stone in the back corner of the cemetery. He had brushed the snow from it and then stood motionless in front of it, before turning and retracing his steps.

There was no name on the grave. Any markings it might have displayed had long since been wiped clean by the elements.

I lost touch with the club members after that. I went off to university, began a career in journalism, started a family, and one by one, the old members died.

But I did meet up with Professor Donald H. Kelly again, two decades later. I was at Harvard for a year on a mid-career journalism fellowship that allowed me to audit any of its courses, and he was an old man, a professor emeritus who delivered a half-dozen lectures a year to a capacity audience in the large Sanders Theatre lecture hall. He still entered with a briefcase at the appointed time, still set his notes on his open and upturned briefcase, and still finished as the Harvard Yard bells struck the hour. His voice wasn't as strong, but his beaming face—it really did resemble a smiling egg—was the same. His lectures were celebrated events on campus. One, in particular, on the subject of North American Indigenous people and attitudes toward them, was conceded to be a highlight of the school year, reducing the lecture hall to tears.

It happened that I dropped by to see him on the day he gave that lecture and found him behind ceiling-high stacks of books in his Widener Library study.

He said he remembered me—"I was working on the 'Silver Screen' lecture, if memory serves, and we strolled on Christmas Eve down to dear old Charlie's house"—and we spoke about our little town and remembered with fondness the club members now departed. He asked me about my young family, and counselled me to remember that a family, above all else, offered true joy in the world.

At one point in our conversation, he was called away, so I had a look around his study.

On his desk—next to his lecture notes—was a book I'd seen before.

A grey cover. A large red ink stain. It was an old English textbook, full of poems and short stories. Opening it, I found on the flyleaf, written in a schoolgirl's careful hand, the following words:

> One day you will come back
> And make me proud
> Of all the things you are.
> Those dreams we dreamed
> Will grow and grow
> Until we reach the stars.

That day was the last I saw or spoke with Professor Donald H. "Eggs" Kelly. He died a few years later, remembered and beloved by his friends and many former students.

There was, however, a postscript.

It came in the form of a phone call from one of his former graduate students—his favourite, a woman born in Vancouver—whom my wife and I had befriended during our year at Harvard. It was several weeks after the professor's death, and our friend said it was a private matter and could I help her out.

"Sure," I said. "What's up?"

"Well, there's a flap around here concerning Professor Kelly's funeral. Actually, there are two flaps," she said. "The big one has to do with the funeral service.

"The service was held at graveside, all the bigwigs and his long-time friends and grad students showed up, and they lowered the casket. Everyone went away to a rented hall where, as per his wishes, we had a bang-up dinner at the expense of the professor's estate. And that was that. There were some great stories told, some good one-liners, and a good time was had by all.

"But later it somehow emerged—one of his long-time friends let it slip, I think—that there hadn't been a body in the casket. There couldn't have been, you see, because the professor had himself cremated. So everybody wants to know, what was in the casket?"

I laughed and said Professor Kelly always did have a good sense of humour.

"Yes, he did, but that's not why I'm phoning you. You see, I received a notice from a Boston law firm last week, and I went to see them, and it turns out Professor Kelly placed a bequest in his will for me."

"That's great," I said. "That's something you can boast about in the faculty club."

"No," she said, "It's not. I'm not allowed to talk about it. I can't divulge what the monetary amount is, or the task I'm to perform to be able to receive it."

"Task?"

"It's why I'm calling. Mariposa is your hometown, right? Same as the professor, it turns out. The bequest involves me travelling to Mariposa and doing something, so I need some of your local knowledge."

She swore me to silence—"at least for a couple of years, okay?"—then dropped the bomb.

"At the lawyer's office, I was presented with an urn," she said. "It's the professor's ashes. Right now, the urn's in my fridge, behind the bottle of Dom Pérignon the professor gave me to open when I'm granted tenure."

"Professor Kelly's in your fridge?" I asked. "What are you supposed to do with him?"

"I'm instructed to take his ashes to Mariposa, rent a boat at a place called the Narrows, take the boat out by myself on Lake Wissanotti, go to a specific location, and scatter his ashes on the lake."

Now I understood.

"This place on the lake where you're to spread his ashes?" I asked. "Is it off to the right of the last starboard buoy coming out of the Narrows?"

"Christ, how the hell do you know that?" she asked.

"And by any chance are you required to read a short poem at this spot?" I asked. "A poem that's—oh, say—six sentences long and ends with the line, 'Until we reach the stars'?"

"How do you know all this?" she demanded. "What's this all about?"

"Relax," I said. "All it means is that your mentor was an old-school romantic. It's a long story, and I'll tell it to you next time you come to the coast to visit us. In the meantime, you should do exactly as he asked. It's what he wanted. It's what he lived his entire life for."

Then I asked what the second flap was.

"Oh, that," she said. "It has to do with his official Harvard obituary.

"The drill for the high-octane profs when they retire," she said, "is that Harvard prepares an academic obituary and the school gives it to the professor so he or she can see that it's complete and accurate. The reason for this is so that when the professor dies, the obituary will flatter both the professor and the school. You know the kind of stuff—'Professor Kelly was a Fellow of the American Academy of Arts and Sciences, a member of the History of Science Society, member of the Antiquarian Society,' that kind of thing, right?"

"Right," I said. "So what's the flap?"

"Well, Professor Kelly added a name to his society affiliations and nobody knows what the hell it is. Faculty's wondering what this mysterious entity is, and how come none of them was ever asked to join, and his students have been searching for it in Cambridge and Boston and New York and Washington and London, and nobody can find the damn thing listed anywhere. Nobody knows where or what this mysterious academic organization of his is."

"What's the name of it?" I asked.

"The Ten Thirty Club," she said.

Epilogue

AND WITH THAT, Bay Street comes to an end.

There's a new and windowless municipal building adjoining the old Mariposa water filtration plant, and across the road, what used to be the wonderful summer dance hall—the Club Pavalon, better known as the Pav—is now a dusty empty lot, and then it's all Mariposa Beach Park.

The aquatheatre still faces up the hill into the park and looks the same. Out behind it—against its back wall that faces the lake—is where everyone used to sneak a drink or a smoke or indulge in a make-out session during band breaks at the Pav, and it still looks and feels the same.

The park itself is magnificent, maybe even better than it was in my time. There are new little buildings sprinkled about the park to replace old little buildings, and the ball diamond has been removed in favour of more lawn space, but the park still has its open picnic pavilion and its little locked-up bandstand, and it's still anchored on its south side by French's hot dog stand, the mustard-yellow-and-red little food and drink shack that would be instantly recognizable to Leacock who used to take a pot of tea there on a summer's afternoon.

The park is full of life.

There are kids on the swings and kids in the water. There's a kid on a towel under a tree reading a book. There are kids growing up here today for whom the world is as young and as fresh and as full of possibilities as it was in my residency. We can smile at the certainty these kids will have their joys in this town. We can pray they sidestep some of life's sorrows. We can hope that their laughter is as loud and ringing as ours used to be.

I'd like to thank you for your company on this stroll through the years. It's always nicer when somebody's along for the journey, when there's a witness to the memorable moments of your life.

I don't offer any morals out of these stories. If you're reading this, you're likely too old to take advice or counsel on the art of living. You'll keep what you want and leave the rest where you found it, same as always. You've picked up your admirable traits and traditions on your own, and they'll have been modified from the ones you first discovered on your street all those years ago. That's just the way of it.

And you could tell your own stories, couldn't you? About your Christmas or your favourite day, when your world was young and fresh and all things were possible?

Maybe next time you're sitting in front of your tree, and it's quiet and you're feeling reflective, you might close your eyes and wander off and pay a visit to your old street and your old town and the people who were part of it.

You can still see and hear them, can't you? The family? The friends? The neighbours? The people who made your days and your life so special?

They're up there among the decorations and lights of the tree.

See them?

High up in the branches?

Yes, that's them.

They're the ones closest to the Christmas star.

It's a wondrous world, isn't it?

Yes. It is.

Acknowledgements

SOME ELEMENTS OF this work have previously appeared in my Christmas stories published in the *Vancouver Sun*. Some quotations and descriptions of people or events in this work first appeared in the editorials and books of James B. Lamb and are used with his kind permission and the permission of his estate.

Quotes and references from Stephen Leacock's *Sunshine Sketches of a Little Town* are from the Collins White Circle Pocket Novel edition (1944).

I've changed the name of my town, of course. The town's real name is no secret but everyone in it can relax if it's the fictional Mariposa. Stephen Leacock literally wrote the book on my town and he declared that Mariposa was really about seventy or eighty towns "with the same square streets and the same maple trees and the same churches and hotels, and everywhere the sunshine of the land of hope."

I've changed most of the names of the residents, too, as Leacock did more than a century ago. As he said, I've "clapped the gaiters of one ecclesiastic round the legs of another, added the sermons of a third and the character of a fourth." Sometimes it's a pretty thin change of name or clothing or conduct, but then Leacock's fabulous Mariposa undertaker—a character he named Golgotha Gingham—was a real undertaker with the marvellous name of Horace "Golgotha" Bingham, and I went to school with his granddaughter.

I'd like to acknowledge the kindness of those Mariposans who, during the course of my fieldwork, lent their support for a lightly fictionalized account of their childhood world. This includes the people I know as Kathy Farrar, Linda Leatherdale, Pat Clark, Steve Jones, Bruce Jones, Brenda Barr, and Paul Stewart.

I'd also thank a motley collection of past and present Mariposans for their personal support and encouragement. This includes Arnie Taylor, Ralph McIntyre, Frank Milligan, Dave Smith, Bob Church, Paul Bailey, Pat McGarvey, Mike Hubbert, and The Jones Boy.

Thanks, too, to friends Ron Riter and Linda Wilson for their professional read of the manuscript, and to the Niemen Fellows (Harvard Class of 1987) who make life loud and fun and argumentative.

The author would be a lonely hermit if not for the best friendship and support of colleagues Pete McMartin, Vaughn Palmer, and Adam Leamy.

Special thanks to Theodora Lamb and Maxwell Lamb who waited for the music.

Most thanks of all to Betsy Lamb, the angel atop the tree.

About the Author

JAMIE LAMB has been a film critic, Ottawa bureau chief, and columnist for the *Vancouver Sun*, and a reporter at the *Orillia Daily Packet & Times*, *Charlottetown Guardian*, *Peterborough Examiner*, *Georgetown Herald*, *Penetanguishene Citizen*, and *Prince George Citizen*. A Nieman Fellow of Journalism at Harvard University, Lamb was a regular commentator on CBC's *Morningside* and Newsworld, has written for numerous Canadian and US magazines, and taught communications seminars at Harvard University, Boston College, the MIT Media Lab, and the US Naval War College.

JOYCE DODDS PHOTOGRAPHY